THE PHYSICS OF ICE

THE PHYSICS OF ICE

E. R. POUNDER

Professor of Physics and Director
Ice Research Projects, McGill University

PERGAMON PRESS

OXFORD · LONDON · EDINBURGH · NEW YORK
PARIS · FRANKFURT

Pergamon Press Ltd., Headington Hill Hall, Oxford
4 & 5 Fitzroy Square, London W.1

Pergamon Press (Scotland) Ltd., 2 & 3 Teviot Place, Edinburgh 1

Pergamon Press Inc., 122 East 55th Street, New York 22, N.Y.

Pergamon Press GmbH, Kaiserstrasse 75, Frankfurt-am-Main

Federal Publications Ltd., Times House, River Valley Rd., Singapore

Samcax Book Services Ltd., Queensway, P.O. Box 2720, Nairobi, Kenya

First edition 1965

Library of Congress Catalog Card No. 65-21141

Set in 10 on 12 pt. Times
and printed in Great Britain by
Blackie and Son Ltd., Bishopbriggs, Glasgow

Contents

9- 11274   v

Preface

In this short book I have attempted to outline the present state of knowledge regarding the structure and properties of ice, together with some information on its occurrence and movement. As is typical of geophysical problems, information on ice is derived from many scientific disciplines—physics, chemistry, meteorology, and oceanography primarily. The title thus reflects the professional bias of the author to some extent. It does imply correctly, however, that the subject matter deals more with the physics (or science) of ice than with the engineering applications.

A word about the level of the book may be useful. The first four chapters are largely descriptive and should be intelligible, I hope, to anyone with a high school background in science. The balance of the book is more technical and I have tried to write for an audience of university undergraduates who have had a few basic courses in mathematics, physics, and chemistry. I cannot hope to have avoided entirely explaining the obvious, and failing to explain clearly the difficult.

During the past decade I have had the opportunity of directing an active research group on ice physics at McGill University, and such competence as this book may display arises from this experience. It is therefore a pleasure to acknowledge the support and encouragement, financial and otherwise, from the Defence Research Board of Canada, which have made this Ice Research Project possible. I should also like to thank my colleague at McGill, Professor M. P. Langleben, whose critical review of the manuscript led to numerous improvements.

Montreal   ELTON R. POUNDER
January 1964

CHAPTER 1

Introduction

SNOW and ice are among the most familiar of natural phenomena to those of us living in northern countries, and one might reasonably expect that their properties would be well understood. As the behaviour of ice is studied throughout this book, it may therefore come as a surprise to discover how many questions relating to this common material remain to be settled. The study of ice thus presents many points of scientific interest as well as being a matter of some economic importance.

1.1 The Freezing of Pure Water

Because water is such a universal constituent of our surroundings, scientists early formed the habit of using it as a standard (e.g. the specific gravity and specific heat of water at certain temperatures are chosen as unity). This was perhaps not the happiest choice because water is certainly one of the most anomalous compounds known to chemistry and physics. A mere list of the ways in which it behaves differently from substances of similar molecular weight would fill pages, and most of the differences are irrelevant for our present subject. Several of them are vital, however. Figure 1 shows the variation in density of water and ice in the normal temperature range occurring on the earth; more detail for water just above the freezing point is shown in Figure 2. It is seen that pure water expands about 9% on freezing. Expansion on freezing is unusual but not unique; the extent of the expansion in water is. If water in a closed container is frozen, enormous pressure develops on the boundaries, an effect discovered the expensive way by many automobile owners and householders.

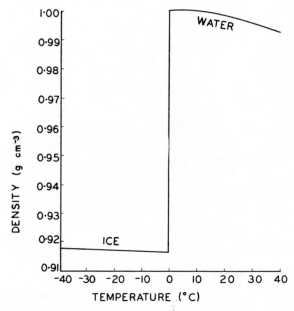

Fig. 1. The densities of ice and air-saturated water at atmospheric pressure.

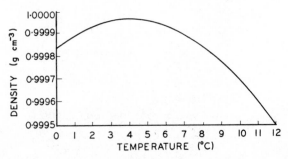

Fig. 2. The density of air-saturated water near the inversion temperature.

Figure 2 shows the existence of a quite extraordinary *inversion temperature* or temperature of maximum density in water at 4°C.

The thermal properties of water are equally anomalous. Both the specific heats of water (1 cal g^{-1}) and ice (0·50 cal g^{-1} at 0°C) and the latent heat of fusion (79·7 cal g^{-1} at 0°C) are abnormally high. Because of this the presence of water and ice exerts a strong ballasting action on temperature variations in any system. On a large scale this results in maritime regions of the earth having less extreme temperatures than inland continental areas. As an example, data from coastal stations on Greenland and interior ones in Siberia, both at a latitude of 70° North, show that the mean monthly temperatures vary in these locations by 20 C deg. and 70 C deg. respectively throughout the year.

1.2 Effect of Impurities

The numerical data of the previous section refer to pure water, but almost all water contains dissolved or suspended impurities, both inorganic salts and organic material. By far the largest part of the surface waters of the earth is in the oceans, which contain enormous quantities of salts. The composition of sea water will be discussed later (section, 2.1) but the important thing is that it is sufficiently uniform that the concentration of salts in sea water can usefully be described by a single parameter, the salinity S, which is defined as the total amount of solid material contained in unit mass of sea water. It is usually quoted as a ratio in g per kg of sea water, that is in parts per thousand, with the abbreviation ‰. A value of $S = 35$‰ is typical of the oceans.

The freezing of such concentrated solutions is a complex process to be enlarged on later. We take as the freezing point the temperature at which ice is in equilibrium with the brine. Then if we assume a constant composition of the brine which is the same as that found in the oceans, the freezing point is an (essentially) linear function of S. So also is the inversion temperature. Figure 3 shows the two lines, which cross at a temperature of $-1·3$°C for $S = 24·7$‰.

Turning now to so-called fresh water, that is the water found in rivers, lakes, springs, etc., the concentrations of impurities are very much smaller, typically a few hundred parts per million. Biologically, these impurities are of great importance. The dissolved salts give water its taste; pure (distilled) water is one of the

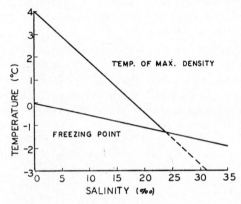

FIG. 3.   The variation of freezing point and inversion temperature with salinity.

dullest of drinks. The organic impurities, including bacteria, determine the potability (or the lack of it) of fresh water. The effect of these impurities on the thermal constants of water and ice (such as the freezing temperature and the specific and latent heats) is usually negligible, but the process of freezing is similar to that occurring in salt water and certain mechanical properties including ultimate strengths are quite sensitive to impurity concentrations. In brief, the freezing of salt water and fresh water differ in degree but not in kind.

1.3   Circulation

Consider a large body of fresh, still water exposed to steadily decreasing air temperatures. We neglect for the moment any horizontal motions of the air or water. When the air becomes cooler than the water, heat is transferred from the topmost layer of water to the air. The cooled water is heavier and sinks, setting up a vertical circulation which continues until the body of water reaches a uniform temperature of 4°C (the inversion temperature). Further cooling of the surface layer reduces its density so that the convective circulation ceases and further heat transfer through the water is by conduction which is a much slower process than convection. Ice soon forms on the surface and reduces heat losses from the water still further since ice is a relatively good heat insulator. A vertical section through a lake in winter shows the following temperature profile. The ice cover usually has a considerable temperature gradient, from the ambient air temperature at the top to 0°C at the bottom of the ice. The top layers of the water show a gradient from 0 to 4°C. This region is called the *thermocline*. The depth of the thermocline depends on the severity of the winter and its duration, but 7 to 10 m is a typical figure for 45° North latitude. Below the thermocline the water is isothermal at 4°C.

This simple one-dimensional model needs slight modifications to describe actual conditions. If there is horizontal motion of the air (wind), the heat transfer from water to air is more rapid because of enhanced evaporation and air turbulence, leading to earlier freezing. On the other hand, if the wind is strong over a deep lake, wind and wave action may result in mixing of the upper layers of water. This has the effect of transporting warmer water to the surface and lowering the depth of the thermocline, thereby delaying the onset of freezing. Some of the Great Lakes of North America (Ontario, Huron, and Superior) never form a complete ice cover for this reason. Even in the absence of a general wind, convective motion of the air takes place as the warmed air over the water rises. This produces an air flow from the land to the water which cools the edges of the body of water more rapidly, causing the initial formation of ice to take place along the shorelines. If the water is in motion (currents), the sharp stratification of water temperatures described above is blurred, and in a shallow turbulent river there may be no thermocline but an almost constant vertical temperature distribution at a temperature very slightly above the freezing point. In deeper rivers, however, there is almost always a slight increase of temperature with depth, although the bottom may be much cooler than 4°C.

If the body of water contains a limited amount of salt (brackish water) the same processes take place as in fresh water except that the temperature below the thermocline will be the temperature of maximum density characteristic of the salinity of the water. If the salinity is greater than 24·7‰ (true sea water) there is no density inversion to limit vertical circulation and the entire body of water must cool to its freezing point before ice can form. For this reason sea ice forms only in high latitudes and after prolonged exposure to cold air. Current and tidal action can modify this simple picture in the oceans. Thermoclines can and do exist, although they are not formed by vertical circulation but are usually associated with salinity gradients (haloclines). Nevertheless, it is not unusual to find an isothermal region, at about $-2°C$, of a few hundred metres in depth below a cover of sea ice.

1.4 The Occurrence and Classification of Ice

Generalizations about the occurrence of ice throughout the world are of limited value because of variations in climate between maritime and continental regions and from continent to continent. In North America most streams and lakes above 35° North usually have some permanent ice cover each winter (reference has already been made to the exceptional behaviour of the Great Lakes) and a similar figure applies to most of Asia. The beneficient effect of the Gulf Stream leaves Ireland, England and most of the southern countries of Europe largely ice free. Extremes of altitude modify conditions, and permanent snow and ice are found on the Andes Mountains at the equator.

In the open ocean, sea ice is of little consequence below 60° of latitude (North or South), but it is a very important factor in somewhat more southerly coastal waters such as Hudson Bay, the Gulf of St Lawrence, the Baltic Sea, and the Sea of Okhotsk. A quasi-permanent cover of sea ice, often referred to as pack ice, exists above about 75° North or South. Drift of sea ice from the Arctic or Antarctic packs (see Chapter 3) or from the mouth of a river (e.g. the St Lawrence) may be a considerable hazard to navigation in quite temperate regions of the oceans.

Classification

The primary division is into sea ice and fresh-water ice. Sea ice may be classified by age into *young ice* (less than 15 cm in thickness and usually formed within the past few weeks), *winter ice* (or annual ice—ice of not more than one winter's growth), *biennial ice* (over one but not over two years in age), and *polar ice* (or perennial ice—over one year old). It may also be classified by the size of unbroken pieces of ice cover into *ice fields* (reaching farther than can be seen from the masthead of a ship), *ice floes* (10 to 2000 m across), *ice cakes* (2 to 10 m across), and *brash* (fragments less than 2 m in diameter). Other descriptions refer to the topography of the ice as smooth, ridged (elevations often up to several metres in height caused by the pressure of the surrounding ice on a field or floe), or *rafted* (when one floe overruns another). For practical reasons most northern countries have developed elaborate terminologies and reporting codes for ice. These have been to some extent standardized through the World Meteorological Organization. An illustrated glossary is given in Armstrong and Roberts (1956).

The sea ice classified above rarely exceeds 4 m in thickness. Also present in the sea may be *icebergs* (large masses of floating or grounded ice. Most of them are fresh and have broken away from glaciers. Occasionally they are formed from ice shelves and are somewhat saline), *tabular bergs* (flat-topped icebergs broken off an ice shelf, particularly in the Antarctic), and *ice islands*. These islands are very large sections from an ice shelf and may be up to 50 m in thickness and 500 km^2 in area. The *ice shelves* themselves are floating ice sheets of considerable thickness, attached on one edge to land. Their origin is still in dispute. The Ward Hunt Ice Shelf on Ellesmere Island in Northern Canada was until recently a strip about 250 km long and up to 50 km wide with an average thickness of about 40 m. Possibly because of shock waves in the atmosphere set up by the Russian nuclear tests on the other side of the Arctic, in 1961 the Ward Hunt Ice Shelf broke up drastically and three or four very large ice islands drifted away. The largest of the ice shelves is the one in the Ross Sea in Antarctica, with an area of about 525,000 km^2, that is slightly larger than Spain. The seaward edge of the Ross Ice Shelf is 500 km long and most of the Shelf is about 400 m thick.

Fresh-water ice is less complex but a few specialized terms may be listed. *Clear ice* is self-explanatory. *Bubbly ice* contains a sufficient number of entrapped air bubbles that it is translucent rather than transparent. *Snow ice* is opaque and milky in appearance. It is formed when snow is flooded with water which re-freezes before the snow melts. *Frazil ice* is one of the first stages in ice formation. It consists of small spicules or disks (with maximum dimensions about 2·5 cm) which form in the top few centimetres of water. The frazil particles aggregate readily. In running water open to cold air (as in a rapids), frazil formation is rapid and constitutes a considerable problem to hydroelectric power development as it tends to block the grills of flume entrances. *Anchor ice* is a peculiar form of ice which freezes on the bottom of a river. The reason for its formation is still unsettled but probably the best theory is that on a clear cold night stones and soil at the bottom of an open river radiate heat through the water sufficiently fast to reach a temperature below 0°C and act as freezing centres. The volume of anchor ice which can be frozen in one night is startling; even more startling is the fact that when the sun rises next morning its radiation frequently releases the attachment of the ice to the bottom. Buoyancy brings the ice to the surface, sometimes to the consternation and hazard of people in small boats.

Glaciology is the study of frozen water in any of its forms or locations. Sometimes the term is used in a restricted sense for the study of glaciers, a large and interesting subject to which little space can be allotted here. In any region where the annual snowfall exceeds the amount of snow melted in summer the snow eventually accumulates to such a depth that it is converted into ice under the pressure of its own weight. Because ice is a plastic material, this *glacial ice* flows slowly to lower elevations. Ice covering a large area and usually moving very little except perhaps at the edges is referred to as an *ice cap*. A stream of more rapidly moving ice, usually flowing down a valley, is called a *glacier*, although the distinction between the two terms is not a sharp one. When a glacier flows into the sea, icebergs often break off or calve from the edge.

Glaciers are very sensitive indicators of climatic change. Almost all the glaciers in the world have been receding and diminishing in size during this century, indicating a gradual warming trend. Glaciation has been far more extensive in the past during several periods called ice ages. The most recent of these, the Wisconsin glacial epoch, ended a little more than 10,000 years ago. At its height, all of Canada, the northern part of the United States, most of the United Kingdom, half of Europe and a large part of northern Asia were all covered with glaciers which were as thick as 3000 m in places. At least four of these ice ages occurred during the last million years and, despite many ingenious theories, it is not known what caused these drastic changes in the climate of the earth.

1.5 Importance of Ice

Probably the greatest importance of ice is biological. Just as snow provides insulation which permits plants and small animals to survive the severity of winter, so the cover of ice over a river or lake prevents the loss of too great a quantity of heat and so protects aquatic flora and fauna. It has often been speculated that if water were like most materials and had a solid state more dense than its liquid form, fresh-water marine life would be impossible in much of the world.

In earlier stages of history, rivers were the principal means of communication, both summer and winter, and ice covers still serve this role occasionally, both as roadways and natural bridges and as landing places for aircraft. Pulp and paper companies use ice covers extensively. Most cutting of pulpwood is done in winter and often the logs are trucked to a river and stored on the ice. When the ice melts in the spring the logs float downriver to the pulp mill.

Refrigeration with ice has a long history but, except in the form of ice cubes, this method of cooling has been replaced largely by mechanical refrigerators. Finally, skating and hockey are popular sports in many parts of the world. Apart from this short list of benefits from ice, its importance is mainly negative. It can make walking and driving difficult, navigation hazardous or impossible, and flooding an annual danger. Ice engineering is principally concerned with the control or removal of ice.

1.6 Special Types of High-pressure Ice

In addition to the ice discussed so far, which we may call normal ice (or ice-I in the Bridgman nomenclature), a number of different types of solid H_2O can be produced artificially by the use of very high pressures. They have been studied mainly by Bridgman (1914, 1937). Except at temperatures lower than those occurring naturally on the earth, none of these ices can exist at pressures of less than 2000 atm. Since the thickest ice sheet in the world—in Antarctica—is less than 4000 m thick, corresponding to a maximum pressure at the base of the ice of about 350 atm, it is clear that none of these artificial ices can normally exist on the earth. Although of considerable interest in the theory of solids, their only practical interest lies in establishing an upper limit to the pressure ice can exert against a pier or dam, or the maximum pressure that can be generated by freezing water in a container. This limit arises because ice-II (and each of the other high-pressures ices) has a specific gravity greater than unity. Hence the pressure cannot exceed about 2000 atm (30,000 psi or about 2000 $kg\ cm^{-2}$) without the phase transition from ice-I to ice-II occurring and preventing any further increase in pressure by a reduction of volume.

CHAPTER 2

Sea Ice

2.1 The Composition of Sea Water

The oceans are salty because rain falling on the land leaches out traces of soluble chemicals from the soil and rock, and eventually carries them out to sea in solution. When the ocean water evaporates, most of the dissolved material is left behind. Since this rain cycle has been going on for some 3×10^9 years or more, sea water contains traces of every chemical element, including those ordinarily considered to be insoluble in water.

Although the concentration of salts in sea water varies slightly from ocean to ocean, the composition is remarkably uniform. A salinity of $34 \cdot 48\%_{\circ}$ is a reasonably good average and is often taken as a standard figure. Let us consider a hypothetical experiment in which exactly 1 kg sea water of this salinity is evaporated, and all water, including water of crystallization driven off. (This experiment would be almost impossible to perform without losing some volatile substances from the dissolved matter as well, and oceanographers use less direct methods.) The solid residue will have a mass of 34·48 g by the definition of salinity, and Table I shows its chemical composition.

TABLE I—COMPOSITION OF SALT FROM 1 KG OF SEA WATER OF
$S = 34 \cdot 48\%_{\circ}$

Salt	NaCl	MgCl$_2$	Na$_2$SO$_4$	CaCl$_2$	KCl	NaHCO$_3$	Other	Total
Mass (g)	23·48	4·98	3·92	1·10	0·66	0·19	0·15	34·48

The trace chemicals grouped under "other" constitute less than 0·5% of the sea salt by weight. Included are elements of great importance biologically but having little influence on the properties of sea ice. In fact these properties are largely controlled by the three major constituents of Table I. It must be emphasized that this table gives the composition of dried sea salt. In solution, the various salts are almost completely ionized and the composition of the sea water is best described in terms of ionic concentrations: $Cl^- = 18·98$, $Na^+ = 10·56$, $SO_4^= = 2·65$, etc., in parts per mille.

2.2. The Freezing of Sea Water

The crystal lattice into which water freezes will be described in detail in Chapter 5. It is a very selective lattice indeed, which will accept no substitutes for hydrogen and oxygen atoms, with the relatively unimportant exception of the fluorine ion. Consequently if an aqueous salt solution (an impure melt in metallurgical terms) is frozen extremely slowly, the foreign ions remain in the melt and perfectly pure ice is formed. The formation of a cover of ice on the surface of the sea is a refining process in which most of the salt is rejected. The freezing rate is usually too rapid for the rejection to approach completion, however, as the growing ice crystals trap a certain amount of brine, cutting it off from the melt. The quantity trapped is a highly variable function of the freezing rate. If the ice cover is broken in the Arctic, and sea water exposed to air temperatures of -30 to $-40°C$ the first ice formed may have a salinity S as high as 20‰ but for a cover of annual ice a typical average figure is $S = 4‰$, that is almost 90% of the salt is rejected during freezing.

The brine retained in sea ice makes it a very different material from pure ice and we must examine the role of the brine in detail, starting with its physical chemistry. Consider first a simple binary system of a solution of sodium chloride in water, which experiences a decreasing temperature. The freezing point, or temperature at which ice starts to form, will be depressed below zero as shown in Fig. 4, which is the phase diagram for this binary mixture. Point A represents brine of 35‰ salinity at 0°C. It must be cooled to -2.1°C before any ice is formed. Once the solid phase appears, there is a unique temperature at which ice and brine of a given concentration (salinity) can exist in equilibrium. If we cool our

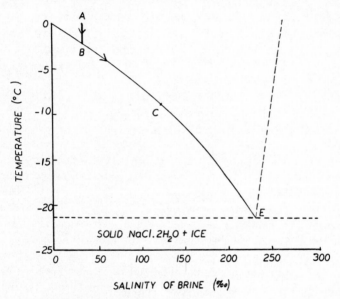

FIG. 4. The phase diagram of a binary system consisting of NaCl and H_2O. Eutectic temperature is -21.1°C.

sample below -2.1°C it must follow this equilibrium line, to C say, where the temperature is -8.5°C and the brine now has $S = 125$‰. In other words, exactly sufficient water must freeze so that the remaining salt and water form a brine of this salinity. As long as the temperature of the sample remains constant this is a stable equilibrium, but an increase in temperature will result in some melting of ice and conversely.

If the temperature is lowered still further, a limit is reached at the point E, called the *eutectic point*. Liquid brine cannot exist below this point, which in the case of sodium chloride brine is at a temperature of $-21 \cdot 1°C$ with a eutectic composition of $233‰$ salinity. The dashed part of the curve is of less interest in connection with sea ice. It shows what happens if the initial composition of the brine is more concentrated than the eutectic composition. For example, if we started with a solution with $S = 250‰$, this solution could be cooled to $-10 \cdot 4°C$ and still remain a liquid. Below this temperature, solid salt would be precipitated in the hydrated form $NaCl.2H_2O$ and the equilibrium point would follow the dashed curve to E. We see thus that regardless of the initial concentration of a sodium chloride brine, below a temperature of $-21 \cdot 1°C$ it will be completely frozen, consisting of a mixture of pure ice crystals and solid sodium chloride dihydrate. Tacit in the above discussion is the assumption that we are dealing with a closed system. In the case of an ice cover on the sea, two different situations arise. At the freezing interface there is a slight increase in salinity because of rejection of salt. However, freezing is usually a slow enough process that mixing by gravity of the heavier, rejected brine with the bulk of the sea water and diffusion prevent any significant increase in salinity. The temperature of the water 1 or 2 cm below the interface almost always equals the freezing point characteristic of the salinity of the ocean as a whole. The other situation occurs in the pockets of brine trapped in the ice cover since these *are* closed systems, and must display the type of behaviour discussed above.

Phase diagrams similar to Fig. 4 can be drawn for any aqueous salt solution, but with different eutectic temperatures (T_E) and compositions. The important ones are: magnesium chloride—$T_E = -33 \cdot 6°C$, precipitated as $MgCl_2.8H_2O$ or $MgCl_2.12H_2O$; sodium sulphate—$T_E = -3 \cdot 5°C$, precipitated as $Na_2SO_4.10H_2O$; calcium chloride—$T_E = -55°C$, precipitated as $CaCl_2.6H_2O$; and potassium chloride—$T_E = -11 \cdot 1°C$, precipitated in anhydrous form. Note that the eutectic temperatures quoted are for binary systems only.

When we go to sea water itself, the situation is more complicated because of the great variety of dissolved materials. When sea water is cooled to slightly below its freezing point, there is at first a true two-phase system consisting of solid H_2O and a uniform brine phase. This simple situation exists down to $-8\cdot2°C$. Below this temperature *some* of the sodium sulphate is precipitated and we have a three-phase system: solid H_2O, solid $Na_2SO_4.10H_2O$, and brine. Note the difference between

$$T_E = -3\cdot55°C$$

for a pure sodium sulphate brine and this critical temperature of $-8\cdot2°C$. Evidently the presence of other solutes in sea water inhibits the precipitation of sodium sulphate. Note also that $-8\cdot2°C$ is *not* a eutectic temperature; it is the temperature at which a solid salt phase *starts* to appear. The next critical temperature is $-22\cdot9°C$ at which $NaCl.2H_2O$ starts to precipitate, leading to a four-phase system. These two temperatures may be expected to be significant in functions relating the physical properties of sea ice to temperature.

Experimental data on sea-water brines below $-30°C$ are too limited to be certain of the exact figures, but it appears that potassium chloride starts to precipitate at $-36\cdot8°C$, $MgCl_2.12H_2O$ at $-43\cdot2°C$, and $CaCl.6H_2O$ at $-54°C$. Further details may be found in Assur (1958). An important fact is that apparently sea ice always contains some liquid at any temperature found naturally on earth—sea ice cooled to $-80°C$ in the laboratory still contained traces of brine.

Because of the great spread in the temperatures at which the various salts precipitate from brine, one might expect some differential salt rejection on freezing of sea water, and it is true that the sulphate–chloride ion ratio in sea ice is higher than it is in sea water. However, the difference is small enough to be neglected for most purposes so that it is an excellent approximation to assume that the salt in sea ice has the same composition as that in the sea water from which it is frozen.

2.3   The Optical Properties of Ice

The study of the internal structure of ice is made easier by its optical properties. Clear ice is quite transparent to visible light. In his compendium on the properties of water in all its phases, Dorsey (1940, p. 490) quotes values for k, the absorptivity, of the order of 6×10^{-3} cm^{-1} for blue light up to 14×10^{-3} cm^{-1} for red light. The absorptivity is defined by the usual exponential law of absorption $I = I_0 \exp(-kx)$ where I is the intensity of light remaining after passage through x cm of ice. If we take

$$k = 10 \times 10^{-3} \text{ cm}^{-1}$$

one metre of ice absorbs about 63 % of the light passing through it. If the ice contains air bubbles or other foreign matter the transmission of light may be considerably reduced by scattering as well. Thus sea ice, particularly at temperatures below $-10°$C, transmits light poorly because of the salt deposits in it.

Another important property is that ice is birefringent. Optically, ice is a uniaxial crystal, the optic axis being the c-axis of crystallographic notation. If light is incident parallel to the c-axis transmission is normal, but if the light is incident at an angle to the c-axis it is separated into the so-called ordinary and extraordinary rays which travel at different speeds in the ice and so are refracted at different angles.

If unpolarized light is passed through a *Polaroid* filter, the emergent light is (largely) plane-polarized. If two such filters are mounted parallel and with their planes of polarization at right angles (the so-called crossed polaroids arrangement), almost no light is transmitted. A mechanical analogy may help in understanding this. Suppose a rope is stretched straight and tight through two slat fences, one with vertical pickets and the other with horizontal bars. If the spaces between the slats are narrow, no transverse vibration of the rope on one side of the system will be transmitted to the other side.

Polarized light is used to study ice structure as follows. A thin section of ice, preferably 1 mm or less in thickness for the clearest results, is placed between crossed polaroids and the light transmitted through the system is viewed. Consider a crystal of ice whose *c*-axis is parallel to the direction of transmission of light.

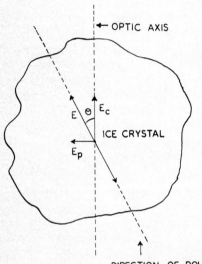

Fig. 5.   Plane polarized light incident on a crystal whose optic axis is perpendicular to the direction of light propagation. The plane of polarization (the plane containing the *E*-vector of the light wave) makes an angle θ with the plane containing the *c*-axis and the propagation vector.

This crystal does not alter the state of polarization of the light, which is thus extinguished by the second or analysing polaroid, and the crystal will appear dark. (In practice, extinction is not complete since the polaroids do not produce completely plane-polarized light.) Consider next a crystal whose *c*-axis is at right angles to the direction of propagation of the light. There will be some angle θ between the *c*-axis and the direction of polarization, as shown in Fig. 5. The electric vector **E** of the light wave, which defines the direction of polarization, can be resolved into components E_c parallel to the c-axis and E_p perpendicular to it. The component E_p is the ordinary ray and E_c the extraordinary one. Before entering the plate of ice the two components were, of course, in phase, but since they travel through the ice at different speeds they are unlikely to be in phase after they emerge. The phase difference will depend on the crystal thickness, and (unless this thickness is such as to give a phase difference which is a multiple of 2π) the two components will combine to give what is called elliptically polarized light. The second polaroid will analyse this light and reject the component polarized perpendicular to the preferred direction of the filter (which is perpendicular to **E** in the plane of Fig. 5), but it will transmit the other component and so the second crystal we have discussed allows some light to go through the system, an amount which depends on the angle θ. Extinction of light will occur for $\theta = 0$ or $90°$.

So far we have considered only two extreme cases, those with the c-axis parallel and perpendicular to the direction of light propagation. The intermediate cases are more complex to analyse because the velocity of the extraordinary ray varies with the angle between its direction of propagation and the direction of the c-axis. Occasional "accidental" extinction may occur for particular combinations of crystal thickness and orientation but usually some light will be transmitted unless the c-axis of the crystal is either parallel or perpendicular to the direction of polarization. Thus a section of ice containing several crystals will be analysed by the crossed-polaroid system described so that each crystal shows up distinctly with a different intensity of transmitted light. If the section of ice is thin enough, the transmitted light may be coloured when white light is used, because of the variation of the velocity of light with wavelength and the resulting differing states of polarization of different colours. These colours are very attractive but incidental, and black and white photographs such as Fig. 6 are used for measurements. This figure shows a photograph in polarized light of a thin section of sea ice. The centimetre scale at the bottom shows that the typical crystal in this section was of the order of 1 × 2 cm. The ovals at the left are air bubbles trapped between the ice section and the lucite plate on which the ice was resting. The sub-structure within each crystal will be discussed later.

The photograph of Fig. 6 was taken in a simple polariscope in which the two polaroid sheets and the section of ice were all

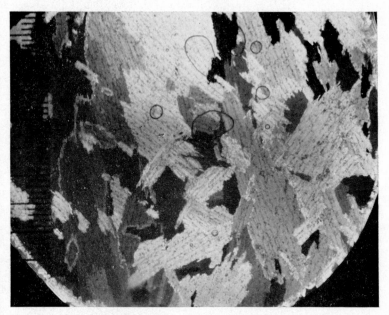

FIG. 6. A thin section of sea ice photographed in polarized light.
The scale is in centimetres.

parallel. If it is necessary to determine the direction of the optic axis of a crystal of ice, this can be done in a polariscope with a universal stage, similar to those used on a microscope in geology but on a considerably larger scale. With this instrument, the piece of ice is mounted on a frame with three degrees of freedom so that the orientation of the sample can be changed at will and measured accurately. By rotating the section of ice in three dimensions, until the polarized light passing through a particular crystal is extinguished, the direction of its c-axis relative to a predetermined coordinate frame can be found. Technical details of the methods used may be found in Langway (1958).

2.4 The Structure of Sea Ice

When the surface of the sea is cooled to its freezing point and further heat is transferred to the atmosphere, small discoids or platelets of pure ice, called *frazil*, form in large numbers in the top few centimetres of water. These platelets are thin, of average size about 2.5 cm $\times$ 0.5 mm, and may vary considerably in shape, from almost square plates to hexagonal dendrites. The c-axis of a platelet is always perpendicular to its plane surface. These elementary ice crystals float to the surface forming a sort of slush and giving the sea initially a slightly oily appearance. In still water the platelets will float with their plane surfaces horizontal, that is with vertical c-axis. Any wind or waves will produce compaction, forcing some of the platelets towards a vertical position. Thus when a continuous cover is formed by the platelets freezing together, they will have a variety of orientations. On first formation, the continuous cover of ice is amazingly flexible. If disturbed by waves from open water or by the wake of a ship, transverse waves of several centimetres amplitude can travel through the ice without fracturing it.

As freezing continues, the platelets act as seed crystals. The detailed mechanism is not understood. As Fig. 6 shows, the ice consists of crystals, where a single crystal is defined as a part of the ice having a high degree of order, including an appearance of uniform brightness in polarized light. The term *grain* is sometimes used instead of single crystal since this structural unit obviously has a complex substructure of many parallel platelets. The relationship of this substructure to the original frazil is obscure. To some extent, no doubt, a crystal is started by compaction of the discoids of frazil which survive as the platelets of the crystal. This cannot be the only process because crystals some-times start to grow on the lower surface of a fairly thick ice cover, and these too show the same platelet structure. Whatever the mechanism, all ice crystals, in fresh-water ice as well as sea ice, are made up of large numbers of platelets quite accurately parallel to each other. Each crystal has a well-defined c-axis perpendicular to the platelets.

A study of the distribution of orientation of the c-axes of the crystals as a function of depth in the cover gives interesting results. The orientation can be described by two angles, a polar angle which is the angle between the c-axis of the ice crystal and the vertical, and an azimuthal angle measured from some arbitrary direction such as north. Except possibly in some unusual tidal situations the azimuthal angle of the c-axis of the ice crystal is completely random. The polar angle, however, shows considerable regularity. As described above, the orientations in the surface layer vary greatly since they depend on wind conditions at the time of freeze-up, but as one proceeds lower in the ice, the average polar angle of the crystals increases steadily until by a depth of 20 cm or so almost all of the crystals have essentially horizontal c-axes. A laboratory study (Perey and Pounder, 1958) of the freezing of distilled water under one-dimensional cooling and still conditions gave the results shown in Table II. Thin horizontal sections were cut at the surface and at depths of 5 and 13 cm. Each section was analysed in a universal stage polariscope and the percentage of the area having crystals with polar angles within 10° ranges was measured.

TABLE II—CRYSTAL ORIENTATION IN AN ICE COVER

Depth (cm)	% of area with polar angles in the range			
	0–10°	10–20°	70–80°	80–90°
0	68	7	6	5
5	12	3	18	26
13	13	2	14	43

Similar results have been found repeatedly in natural sea ice and there is no reason to doubt that annual sea ice always shows this pattern except when extensive rafting or pressure ridging occurred during its growth. Thus the bulk of a cover of annual sea ice consists of crystals with horizontal *c*-axes randomly

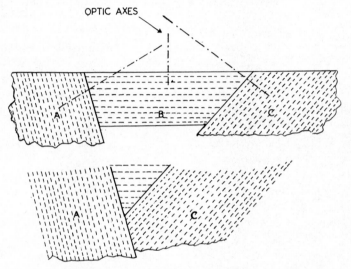

Fig. 7.   Preferred growth of crystals with inclined optic axes, resulting in gradual extinction of a vertically oriented crystal. The lower sketch shows a later stage in freezing.

oriented in azimuth. These crystals usually have much greater vertical height (up to 1 m or more) than diameter ($\sim$ 1 to 5 cm).

Figure 7 shows an explanation for the preference for horizontal *c*-axes. Since an ice crystal has one main axis of symmetry it may grow in essentially two directions, by adding molecules to the lattice in existing planes perpendicular to the *c*-axis, the *basal planes*, or by adding them in the direction of the *c*-axis leading to additional basal planes in the lattice. On thermodynamic grounds, one would expect the first method of growth to be slightly favoured and this has been proved experimentally. Figure 7 shows three crystals, the dotted lines being the basal planes. Preferred growth along the basal planes leads to the extinction of the middle crystal *B* which is ultimately cut off from the melt. After this stage, more rapid growth of crystal *A* at the expense of *C* will occur.

A similar analysis of the variation of crystal size with depth shows less regularity. Crystals near the surface tend to be small, with a gradual increase in horizontal dimensions with depth. Figure 8 shows a vertical section taken from a piece of Arctic sea ice at a depth of 1·7 m. A number of small crystals are visible as inclusions in the larger ones. These are quite common, particularly when the freezing rate increases because of an earlier air temperature drop. Unless the new crystals have the favoured orientation with horizontal *c*-axes they do not grow to any appreciable size.

The Ice–Water Interface

Examination of the lower surface of a growing sheet of sea ice gives considerable insight into the mechanism involved in freezing. The lower 1 to 2 cm consists of pure ice platelets with layers of brine between them. The platelets which form part of a single crystal are accurately parallel, and usually vertical. This structure is called the skeleton layer. Its mechanical strength is negligible. As freezing continues, the platelets thicken up slightly and ice bridges develop between them, gradually forming an almost solid structure. As the solid interconnections develop, brine is trapped in pockets or cells between the platelets. The brine cells shrink in size as the ice cools, tending towards long vertical cylinders of almost microscopic cross-section. These can be seen in Fig. 6 as rows of black dots along the lines between platelets. Some brine cells are also found at intercrystalline boundaries, but we can see from Fig. 6 that a large majority of the brine is within the individual grains.

Figure 9 gives the results of statistical study of the platelet thicknesses in a sample of annual sea ice, showing that the platelets are quite uniform with an average thickness of 0·5 to 0·6 mm.

Fig. 8. Vertical section of a cover of Arctic sea ice photographed in polarized light. The photograph is oriented with the upper layer of ice at the top. The length of the section is 15 cm and its centre was 1·7 m below the surface of the ice.

The typical brine pocket diameter is about 0·05 mm. The length of brine pockets is considerably more variable than their diameters, and not as well known. The order of magnitude of this length is probably about 3 cm.

We thus see that most sea ice consists of macroscopic crystals with a complex internal structure of platelets of pure ice and large numbers of brine cells. In addition, there are usually many small,

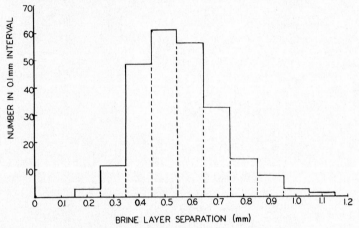

Fig. 9. Statistics of platelet thickness in annual sea ice.

spherical air bubbles in the ice, formed when the air dissolved in sea water is released as the water freezes. The fraction of the volume of a piece of sea ice occupied by fluid, brine or air, is an important parameter called the *brine content*, v. It is calculable from a knowledge of the salinity, temperature and density of the sea ice. On the basis of present knowledge of the phase relations at low temperatures of the brines in sea water, Assur (1958, p. 138) has calculated v for a useful range of salinity and temperature values. His results make no provision for air bubbles, but their contribution to v can be calculated experimentally from a comparison of the density of a sea ice sample with the density of pure ice at the same temperature.

2

The Variation of Salinity with Time

Sea ice in nature is virtually never in an equilibrium state. We shall see that most of its physical properties depend on the brine content v, and this parameter varies with time because of both temperature and salinity changes. The salinity of sea ice changes in two ways. At least at temperatures above $-15°C$, the brine

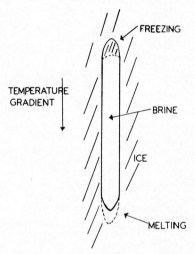

FIG. 10. Brine migration along the temperature gradient.

cells have some interconnections so that brine may drain slowly through the ice under the influence of gravity. A piece of sea ice cut out from an ice cover and stored at $-15°C$ or higher, gradually "bleeds" brine, the rate of discharge of the brine increasing rapidly with temperature as the brine cells become enlarged.

If there is any temperature gradient in sea ice (as is virtually always the case), the brine cells migrate along the gradient in the direction of higher temperature. In Fig. 10, consider a long vertical brine cell, and the usual temperature condition, namely that the ice–air interface is colder than the bottom of the ice sheet, which is fixed at the freezing point of the sea water. Because of diffusion the concentration of brine within the cell will be uniform, and of a salinity to match the mean temperature of the ice surrounding the cell. Hence at the warmer end the brine is too concentrated and will dissolve ice to reduce its concentration. At the colder end more ice freezes to increase the brine concentration, and the net effect is to move the entire cell of brine along the gradient. This effect was demonstrated in a striking fashion by Whitman (1926) who forced brine to migrate upwards against gravity by applying a large vertical temperature gradient. In a sea ice cover the brine migration acts in the same direction as brine drainage so that the two effects are additive. Both processes take place slowly, but at a measurable rate, in an ice cover during the winter months. Brine drainage is quite rapid when the ice approaches its melting point. If a block of ice is removed from contact with the sea, as by being pushed up on shore, it loses salt very rapidly during the warmer months of spring and summer.

Consider now the state of an annual ice floe in the Arctic Ocean which does not melt completely during the brief and cold summer. For a period of a month or so it is at an almost uniform temperature only slightly below its freezing point. The brine cells are enlarged, and so interconnected with each other and the sea that the ice sheet is saturated with sea water; a hole dug in a floe in summer fills with sea water up to the hydrostatic level in a matter of seconds. This sea water is presumably in the channels in the ice which the brine cells formed, and the effect is to replace the concentrated brine of the winter ice by sea water of normal salinity, without a proportional increase in the size of the brine cells. Since this is what happens, it is clear that the various processes of ice melting, brine drainage, and diffusion are *not* taking place in thermodynamic equilibrium. When the temperature of the ice drops again, brine cells get cut off from each other and from the sea, and decrease in size to smaller diameters than they had the previous winter. The floe is now called polar ice and its salinity is much lower than that of annual ice. This removal of salt from sea ice may continue during a second summer; this is not certain, but in any event most of it is removed during the first year. Recently the author compared ice known to be about eighteen months old with several-year-old polar ice. Their salinities were $1\%_0$ and $0.5\%_0$ respectively, in contrast with the typical $4\%_0$ of annual ice. The Eskimos have long known that potable water can be obtained by melting sea ice which is over a year old.

2.5 Polar Ice

The surface of the Arctic Ocean and part of the adjoining seas, and the regions surrounding the Antarctic continent are almost entirely covered the year round with polar ice which is several years in age, and which has a very characteristic appearance. When it has no snow cover it appears to be pale blue in colour in contrast with the greyish white of annual sea ice. A polar floe is rarely level, but is covered with gently rounded hummocks of the order of 1 m in height, spaced 30 to 40 m apart. The drift of the pack ice and the resulting pressure ridging will be discussed in the next chapter. Here we shall consider something of the history of an individual ice floe. Ice will form in the fall on open water and grow as annual sea ice the first winter to a thickness of 2 to 3 m. During the next summer it will reject salt as described in the last section and become polar ice with a low salinity. Considerable surface melting occurs, and, since the floe is likely to have some slight surface irregularity, the melt water will collect in pools. The albedo (reflecting power) of the water is lower than that of the wet snow on the higher parts of the surface, so that more solar energy will be absorbed by the water, leading to increased melting below and around these pools. It is this differential melting of the surface which, over a period of years, produces the hummocky contours of a polar floe.

Some of the melt water spills over the edges of the floe or runs down through cracks. This melt water is essentially fresh and so less dense than sea water. Eventually it mixes with the sea water, but there is usually a layer of fresh water immediately below a polar floe in summer. Since the freezing point of the fresh water is higher than that of sea water, it may become cooled sufficiently to freeze to the bottom of the floe. When cold weather comes again, sea ice grows once more on the bottom. This cyclic process of surface melting in summer and freezing on the lower side in winter continues as long as the floe stays in a climate cold enough that it never melts completely, and an equilibrium thickness of 3 to 4 m is reached in a few years. Any particular plane of ice moves gradually upwards; ice at a depth of 2 m today will form part of the surface 2 or 3 years from now. There are, of course, considerable variations from the average thickness of 3·5 m quoted, because of climatic variations, effect of rafting, and so on —ice floes over 5 m thick are found frequently.

Because of its complex history, polar ice shows less regularity in its crystal structure than annual sea ice. Crystals tend to be smaller, and it is reported that in some old polar ice the platelet structure largely disappears.

Finally, it should be pointed out that polar ice is extremely hard. Its compressional strength is so great that ice-breaker captains have learned by experience (sometimes bitter) that polar floes may be pushed aside but that any attempt to break them is dangerous.

2.6   The Structure of Fresh-water Ice

It was stated earlier that the types of ice formed from salt water and fresh water differ in degree but not in kind, so a chapter on sea ice is a logical place to discuss the structure of fresh-water ice, in terms of how it differs from sea ice. The impurity concentration in fresh water is so much lower than in sea water that fresh-water ice is a relatively homogeneous material with fairly constant physical properties. It shows the same type of platelet structure within its crystals, as was first noted by Faraday in 1860, but the platelet thickness is an order of magnitude less than in sea ice, Nakaya (1956) finding a mean thickness of 0 061 mm.

What impurities there are in fresh-water ice seem to be concentrated largely though not entirely in the grain boundaries instead of mostly in the platelet boundaries as in sea ice. The two types of ice decay in different fashions for this reason. Sea ice melts initially by enlargement of the brine cells. Since these exist in very large numbers, the entire structure of sea ice weakens and becomes rotten before there is any major change in the appearance of the ice. Fresh-water ice on the other hand decays first at the grain boundaries. The grains or crystals of fresh-water ice are usually long vertical cylinders, which thus tend to separate. Decaying fresh-water ice is often referred to as "candled" because of its resemblance to a pile of closely packed wax candles.

One major difference from sea ice lies in the orientation of the optic axes of the crystals. We have seen that in sea ice the surface layer usually has crystals with predominantly vertical c-axes but that lower in the ice cover the orientation is almost completely horizontal. We choose, somewhat arbitrarily, to call this the "normal" crystal structure of ice. Numerous studies of ice on fresh-water lakes show that the normal pattern occurs here much of the time, but that an "anomalous" crystal structure in which the entire ice cover consists of relatively large crystals with vertical optic axes can also occur. Lake ice apparently has one or other of these structures, with no in-between cases. No completely satisfactory explanation of this phenomenon has appeared. It is known that sill conditions and impure water favour the normal pattern— solutions of salinity as low as 1‰ always freeze "normally" if there is no disturbance during freezing. Studies of the details of the freezing process in ice form an active research field at present, a field which is closely related (except in freezing temperatures) to metallurgical work on freezing from impure melts.

CHAPTER 3

Ice Drift

SUMMARIES of variable geophysical features, such as climatic, oceanographic, and ice cover data, can easily be misleading if taken too literally. Only averages can be quoted, and one of the near certainties in this uncertain world is that local conditions at a given place and time will not be average. Nevertheless it seems of interest to discuss briefly the great ice packs of the polar regions and their movements. The first two sections will deal with the Arctic and Antarctic packs, and then icebergs will be treated separately—their greater depth causes them to move in a different fashion, to penetrate farther into temperate regions, and hence to constitute a greater menace to ordinary shipping.

At the outset the contrast between the Arctic and Antarctic regions should be noted. In addition to being opposite in latitude they are also opposite in almost every other way. The Arctic Basin contains a great mediterranean ocean 2000 miles (3200 km) across, with narrow channels connecting it with the Atlantic and Pacific Oceans. Antarctica is a continent, almost 3000 miles (4800 km) across, surrounded by an ocean with no land divisions from the Atlantic, Pacific and Indian Oceans. Most of the land around the Arctic Ocean is quite low; Antarctica, with a mean height of about 6000 ft (1800 m) and peaks over 13,000 ft, is the highest of the continents. The Arctic, contrary to popular belief, is not desperately cold, with minimum temperatures only rarely below $-50°F$ ($-47°C$); Antarctica is the coldest place on earth— a temperature of $-105°F$ ($-74°C$) was recorded at the South Pole during the International Geophysical Year (I.G.Y.) of 1957–8.

3.1 Arctic Pack Ice

Most of us are so familiar with the stillness of a frozen lake or small river that we unconsciously think of an ice cover as a permanent thing in winter, with ice movement being a feature of the spring break-up. In the oceans and some of the great northern rivers like the St Lawrence this is not the case; the forces on the ice caused by wind, water currents, and tides are too great to permit the formation or maintenance of a continuous cover. Instead the ice consists of individual pieces ranging widely in size from ice fields to small fragments. On a local scale their motion usually appears to be chaotic with pieces bumping into and sometimes overriding each other to produce rafted ice. If the ice movement in a region is convergent, that is if the forces involved act to increase the quantity of ice in the area, eventually pressure ridges develop. To watch thousands of tons of ice lift slowly and noisily upwards gives one a stronger feeling for the magnitude of natural forces than any description can convey. Pressure ridges with a height of 8 to 10 m are occasionally seen in the Arctic although the majority are considerably smaller than this. Traversing the Arctic pack one usually encounters up to 4 or 5 pressure ridges per kilometre, but the number may rise to 30 per kilometre in places.

River Ice

On a larger scale, ice drift follows a pattern, which depends on the average meteorological and oceanographic conditions, and it is this pattern we wish to discuss. Rivers are normally fairly simple and we shall give a brief description of the St Lawrence, the river with which the author is most familiar (see Fig. 11). The flow varies between 150,000 and 300,000 $ft^3 sec^{-1}$ to make it a remarkably well-behaved river. The head between Montreal and the Atlantic, a distance of about 900 miles, is only 90 ft so that currents are slight in this region. Tidal effects are observable up to

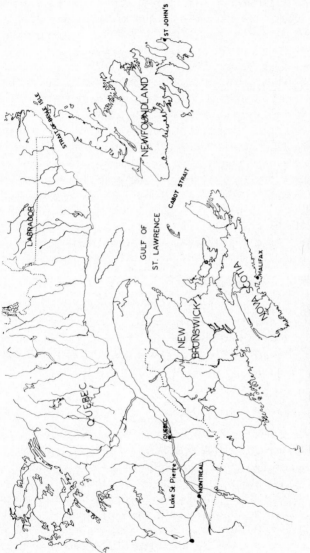

FIG. 11. The St Lawrence River (below Montreal) and the Gulf area.

Lac St Pierre (800 miles from the sea) but the water is saline only below Quebec, another 100 miles downriver. The maximum tidal range in the river is about 23 ft. The ice cover is rarely continuous below the head of tidal waters, and never so in the Gulf of St Lawrence, a large estuary of roughly 4×10^4 square miles in area with a salinity virtually that of the Atlantic Ocean. The dominant factor in ice movement in the Gulf is wind and since the prevailing wind is northwest, there is usually a relatively free channel 10 or 15 miles wide along the north shore of the Gulf. This channel is put to good use by the winter shipping in the Gulf area which has become an important factor in the Canadian economy since 1955.

Nevertheless, the discharge of the river to the ocean must take place and must carry ice with it. The flow through the Strait of Belle Isle, a very narrow deep passage between Newfoundland and the mainland of Canada, is into the Gulf, so the egress takes place through Cabot Strait. This strait is blocked with ice most of the winter, and shipping into the Gulf in the December–March period usually must be convoyed by an icebreaker. The ice from the Gulf melts fairly soon after entering the Atlantic Ocean but often causes shipping difficulties for ports on the south coast of Newfoundland and the extreme north-east of Nova Scotia. The east coast of Newfoundland must often contend with Labrador ice moving down from the north-west, and the harbour of St John's has been blocked by ice as late as the early part of July.

Drifting Stations

Knowledge of ice movement in the Arctic is relatively extensive for such a vast, remote region, and is largely based on some twenty drifting stations which have been set up and manned for long periods during the last eighty years. At first these were ships which ventured into the Arctic Ocean (see Fig. 12) and drifted (not always intentionally) with the pack. Several ships were destroyed by the ice and in this work, as in other phases of polar exploration, there was considerable loss of life. The first successful scientific drifting station was the cruise of the *Fram* in 1893–6.

This expedition was led by Dr. Fridtjof Nansen. The ship was sailed through Bering Strait and deliberately frozen into the pack in the region of the New Siberian Islands. She drifted with the pack without damage and three years later broke free of the ice not far from Spitsbergen, having been carried across the Arctic Ocean on the Siberian side of the North Pole. No mention of the

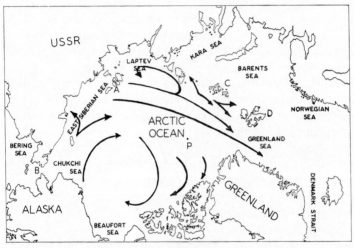

FIG. 12.   Ice drift in the Arctic Ocean. The arrows show the average direction of ice movement in each region. Several locations are marked by letters: *A*—the New Siberian Islands, *B*—the Bering Strait, *C*—Franz Josef Land, *D*—Spitsbergen, and *P*—the North Pole.

voyage of the *Fram* would be complete without a reference to Nansen's incredible journey. He was a man who was a firm believer in burning bridges behind himself, so when it became apparent that the *Fram* would not drift near the North Pole, he left the ship under the command of Otto Sverdrup, and he and one other man, F. H. Johansen, set out to walk to the North Pole, knowing that they could never find the ship again because of its uncertain drift. They didn't reach the Pole but were forced to turn back at 86° North and to make for Franz Josef Land where they spent the winter. The next summer they were rescued, accidentally, by a British expedition. Oddly enough, Nansen and his companion reached Norway within a week of the arrival of the *Fram*. Other important shipboard drifting stations included the Norwegian *Maud* in 1918–25 and the Russian icebreaker *Sedov* in 1937–9.

Improvements in aircraft changed the approach to one of establishing camps on the ice itself, camps which could be established and maintained by air. Evacuation of personnel is also usually by air, or occasionally by icebreaker when a camp drifts near the edge of the ice pack. The Russians were the pioneers in this type of drifting station. Station North Pole I (N.P. I) was established in 1937, and followed by about ten other N.P. stations in the period 1950–63. Most of these camps were set up on sea-ice floes, although one (N.P. VI) was on an ice island. The period of occupation of each station has varied, but has usually been slightly over a year.

In 1947 the United States Air Force started regular weather reporting flights over the Arctic Ocean. One of the first results of this programme was the discovery of a series of ice islands which were given the designations T–1, T–2, T–3, this last one often being called Fletcher's Ice Island after its discoverer. It is an island about 50 to 60 m thick, with a surface of about 14 km by 8 km. Since ice islands can be distinguished from the air, their positions were recorded frequently on reconnaissance flights. Being much larger and deeper than sea ice floes, ice islands do not drift with quite the same velocities as the adjoining sea ice. In 1952, the U.S.A.F. set up a camp on T–3 for meteorological and other geophysical observations and this station has been occupied since then except for two brief periods. It was one of three American drifting stations in the Arctic during I.G.Y., the other two being on ice floes. Two other drifting stations, one on a floe and one on another ice island, were occupied by American parties after the I.G.Y. period. As with the Russian stations, each camp was maintained for 12–18 months.

One other important type of research platform in the Arctic is the nuclear submarine. Since the submarine cruises at a considerable depth below the ice, this American programme of polar voyages has not yielded too much information about ice drift, but it has been extremely valuable in studying the bathymetry and oceanography of the Arctic Ocean and the Canadian Archipelago, and in giving information on the bottom contours of the ice and its thickness.

The first serious proponent of the submarine as a vessel for Arctic exploration was Sir Hubert Wilkins who in 1931 obtained a submarine, which he called the *Nautilus*, and tried to take it under the Arctic ice cover. This expedition was not very successful, mainly because the submarine of that day could only submerge for such a brief period, and practical under-ice operations had to wait for the U.S. nuclear submarines with their capacity to submerge to great depths and to cruise submerged for indefinitely long periods. The first of these was named, inevitably, the *USS Nautilus* and did indeed make most of Jules Verne's dreams come true. In the summer of 1957 she entered the Arctic Ocean through the Bering Strait and penetrated almost as far as the Pole. The trip through the Bering Strait proved difficult because of the extreme shallowness of the water, often little over 100 ft deep, and the depth of the great pinnacles of ice which reach down from the ice cover in places. The next year, in August 1958, the *Nautilus*, under the command of Commander William Anderson, made a complete transit under the Arctic ice pack, passing directly over the North Pole. The entire trip from Pearl Harbor to Portsmouth, England—a distance of over 8000 miles—took 20 days and was carried out almost entirely underwater. The Arctic Ocean part of it included 1800 miles under the ice and was made in 4 days.

Other Arctic voyages have been made by the U.S. nuclear submarines *Skate*, *Sargo*, and *Seadragon*. In 1958, *Skate* proved that it was possible to surface almost at will in summer in open water among the pack ice. With *Sargo* it was shown to be possible to surface in winter by finding a refrozen lead. The Arctic submarines have a reinforced conning tower, or "sail" as it is now called, and can safely break through sea ice 3 ft thick. In 1960, *Seadragon* made a submerged trip from west to east through Parry

Channel (the Northwest Passage through the Canadian Arctic Islands at 75° North). With continual improvement in their scientific equipment being made, these submarines should be an ever more valuable source of information about the Arctic Ocean as well as more temperate water.

Ice Drift in the Arctic Ocean

Figure 12 shows an overall picture of the ice movements in the Polar Basin. The arrows show that there are two main features, an east to west drift on the Russian side of the North Pole and a clockwise circulation called the Beaufort Gyral in the area between Alaska and Canada and the Pole. The first of these is the drift which carried the *Fram*, and the time for a crossing of the Arctic Ocean into the Greenland Sea is about 3 years. This drift discharges great masses of polar ice into the North Atlantic, mostly through the Denmark Strait between Iceland and Greenland. This ice movement makes the approaches to East Greenland difficult. Each year pack ice reaches and rounds Cape Farewell, the southern tip of Greenland. Usually this polar ice does not penetrate far into the Labrador Sea between Greenland and Labrador, or into Davis Strait to the west of Greenland. Figure 12 also indicates sketchily that ice tends to break off the Eurasian side of this broad river of ice and to enter the Laptev, Kara, and Barents Seas where there are complex local circulation patterns. These seas and the ice in them have been studied extensively by the Russians because of the great importance to them of shipping along the Northern Sea Route which extends along the north coast of U.S.S.R. from Murmansk to the Bering Strait.

The pattern of ice movement on the North American side of the Arctic is quite different. Ice may circulate indefinitely in the Beaufort Gyral. On the outer edges the period of revolution is about 10 years, whereas near its centre a round trip may take only 3 or 4 years. Ice moving on the outer part of this system may become involved in the great westward flow of the central Arctic Ocean and be discharged into the Atlantic. It is believed that a substantial but unknown portion of the ice in the Gyral is removed in this way each year. A smaller amount moves out of the Arctic Ocean through the channels in the Canadian Archipelago, particularly into McClure Strait which is the west end of Parry Channel.

At this point it is perhaps worth repeating the warning given at the beginning of this chapter about taking a diagram like Fig. 12 too literally. The various drifting stations did not follow straight-line or smoothly curved paths. Browne and Crary (1958, pp. 192, 193) give a detailed map of the path of T–3 during 1952–5. The island meandered in a most erratic fashion. This is characteristic of most of the drifting stations and so, presumably, of the individual floes making up the pack. Figure 12 gives only long-term average motions.

Theories of Ice Drift

A uniform cake or floe of ice will float in hydrostatic equilibrium at a level determined by the relative densities of the ice and water. The density of Arctic sea water can be considered as relatively constants and equal to $1·025$ g cm^{-3}. The specific gravity of sea ice varies between $0·85$ and $0·93$ and that of fresh-water ice is about $0·917$. Thus fresh-water ice floats in sea water with $0·105$ of its thickness above the surface, and for sea ice of specific gravity $0·890$ the comparable figure is $0·131$. In round numbers, fresh-water ice floats with 90% of its volume below the surface and sea ice is 87% submerged.

Ice is a relatively plastic material, so that if the upper surface of a floe were hummocky or ridged and the bottom surface smooth, in time the high points would sag and produce some relief on the bottom. For complete hydrostatic equilibrium at every point on the floe, the relief of the bottom should match that of the top surface but be magnified in scale by a factor of between 8 and 9. In the ice pack there is so much interaction between floes that the complete equilibrium state never has time to develop, but studies from the submarines show that there is a definite relationship between the height of ridges rising above the general ice level and the depth of ice below the ridge. The depth of the pendant ice below the normal lower ice surface is from three to five times the height of the ridge. Ridges of height about 8 m are often seen, with ice pinnacles up to 30 or 40 m deep below them.

An ice floe in the pack is subjected to four forces:

(1) Wind drag, which is a frictional force between the moving air and the rough surface of the ice. In much of the Arctic Ocean this is the main driving force which keeps the ice in motion.

(2) Water drag, the frictional force between the rough lower boundary of the ice and the water. If there is no water current this is a retarding force slowing down the movement of the ice. In some parts of the Arctic, however, the currents are large, and as important as the wind in causing ice drift, or even more important. Wind and current are frequently not independent forces since the wind tends to drive the surface water, interacting with it in ice-free places as well as by a coupling through the moving ice. The current pattern in the Beaufort Gyral is a clockwise rotation, resulting primarily from the fact that this area of the Polar Basin is covered by a semi-permanent high pressure area and hence has a clockwise wind circulation.

(3) Coriolis force, a force resulting from the earth's rotation, which acts at right angles to the velocity vector of the ice and tries to move it to the right of this direction (in the Northern Hemisphere).

(4) Lateral forces resulting from the pressure of the surrounding ice floes.

Drag forces such as (1) and (2) are usually calculated from semi-empirical formulae, in the present state of knowledge of aerodynamics and hydrodynamics. For example, in an adiabatic atmosphere, the wind drag is usually calculated from Prandtl's equation

$$\tau_a = 0 \cdot 145 \rho_a v^2 \Big/ \left[\ln \frac{z + z_0}{z_0} \right]^2 \tag{1}$$

where ρ_a is the density of the air, v is the wind speed measured at height z, and τ_a is the wind stress. The "roughness parameter",

z_0, is a measure of the unevenness of the surface of the ice, and is usually taken as 3% of the average height of the hummocks above the "level" floe surface. The difficulty of using equation (1) accurately lies in knowing what value of z_0 to apply. A further complication is that the Arctic atmosphere is usually more stable than an adiabatic one, so that the logarithmic variation of wind speed with height, on which equation (1) is based, is not quite accurate and the equation needs slight modification. A similar equation can be used for the water drag but with even greater uncertainty in the appropriate value to use for the roughness parameter, plus the additional difficulty that the direction of the water stress is usually not known accurately.

The one force which can be calculated with some precision is the Coriolis force. The origin of this force can be seen qualitatively as follows. Since the earth is rotating from west to east at a constant angular velocity ω, every point or object fixed in its surface has an eastward velocity $\mathbf{v}_E = \mathbf{v}_0 \cos \psi$ where ψ is the latitude. The eastward velocity of a point on the equator, $\mathbf{v}_0$, has a magnitude $r\omega$ where r is the radius of the earth. This magnitude is a little over 1000 m.p.h. To say that an ice floe is stationary with respect to the earth simply means that it has this correct eastward velocity and no north–south motion. If now the forces of wind and current move the floe to the south, it will maintain the same value of $\mathbf{v}_E$, which will now be too slow for it to keep pace with its new surroundings, since ψ is now smaller and hence $\cos \psi$ larger. Thus the floe tends to lag, and acts as if a force were pushing it westward. This is the Coriolis force, $\mathbf{C}$. We have considered only the simplest case here, but it is shown in books on mechanics that any object in the Northern Hemisphere, moving with a velocity $\mathbf{u}$ with respect to the earth's surface, acts as if there were a Coriolis force on it directed 90° to the right of $\mathbf{u}$. The magnitude of this force is

$$\mathbf{C} = 2m\omega\mathbf{u} \ \sin \psi \qquad (2)$$

where m is the mass of the object. For an ice floe, if the density and thickness of the ice are known, this equation can be used to calculate the Coriolis force per unit area, or stress. The only difference in the Southern Hemisphere is that the force acts to the left of the velocity rather than to the right.

The fourth force, the lateral thrusts of the surrounding ice, will obviously be extremely variable and difficult to predict. In their careful analysis of the movements of T–3, Browne and Crary found that the vector sum of the three forces discussed above could not account for the motion of the island for the entire period of observation. With a reasonable choice of parameter in the theoretical equation, there was fair agreement for the movements of T–3 in 1952 when it was north of 86° North, but the theoretical predictions did not fit the observed data in 1953–4 when the island moved south from 86° North towards Ellesmere Island. Browne and Crary concluded that the convergence of the ice pack could cause lateral forces having a significant effect on ice drift.

In recent years, Wittman and others of the U.S. Hydrographic Office have had some success in predicting convergences and divergences of the pack ice in the Arctic from climatic data and synoptic weather observations. This should lead in time to greater ability to predict ice movements, but enough has been said to indicate the difficulties, so that it is not surprising that most predictions at present are based on a completely empirical approach called Zubov's rule. From an analysis of the drift of the *Sedov*, Zubov concluded that ice drifts along the direction of the isobars on the weather map at a speed proportional to the gradient of the air pressure. In mathematical form the rule is

$$V = \alpha_i \Delta p \tag{3}$$

where V is the drift of ice in kilometres per month, Δp is the pressure gradient in millibars per kilometre calculated from an average monthly map, and α_i is called the isobaric coefficient. Zubov's original value for α_i was improved by Buinitsky who found that it averages 9100 for the period February to April and 12,900 from August to October. Zubov's rule appears to work reasonably well in most of the Arctic, even though it neglects water currents entirely. The probable reasons for its success depend on the existence of a dominant high pressure area over the Arctic Ocean, already mentioned. The wind aloft, the geostrophic wind, blows along the isobars, but because of friction the wind at the surface in a high pressure area blows out from the high, that is at a large angle (up to 45°) to the left of the isobaric direction. This would be the direction of ice drift were it not for the effect of Coriolis force which, acting at right angles to the drift velocity, tries to force the ice back towards the isobaric direction. Apparently wind and Coriolis forces combine to give an ice drift nearly parallel to the isobars.

Water Movements in the Arctic

Throughout most of the Arctic surface currents seem to be a minor factor in ice movements, and the patterns of general air circulation, water currents, and ice drift coincide quite closely. The discharge of ice into the Atlantic, however, is largely carried by the main discharge of water from the Arctic, the East Greenland Current. Zubov and Karelin have estimated the annual inflow of water into the Arctic as 86,000 km^3 (61,000 from the Atlantic, 20,000 from the Pacific, and the balance from river drainage and precipitation). Most of the Atlantic water enters at great depths. The East Greenland Current is estimated to carry 80,000 km^3 of water and 10,000 km^3 of ice out of the Arctic annually.

For further information on ice movements, the reader is referred to three papers in *Arctic Sea Ice*: the paper by Browne and Crary already mentioned and papers by Gordienko (1958) and Fukutomi (1958).

3.2 Antarctic Pack Ice

The Antarctic continent is permanently covered by snow and ice, often of great depth, and surrounded by shorefast ice which may extend a hundred miles or more out from the shore of the continent. Beyond the shorefast ice lies the pack ice which is a mixture of sea ice, fragments broken off from the shorefast ice, and pieces of disintegrated land ice. The extent of the pack varies with the seasons. It is estimated to cover about 23×10^6 km^2 in winter and spring (July to October), and to reduce to an area of 4×10^6 km^2 in the autumn months of February and March. The maximum northern boundary of the pack is quite variable with longitude, reaching to about 55° South in the Atlantic and about 64° South in the Pacific. There is also considerable variation from year to year.

The continent is normally covered with a vast high pressure area of intensely cold air which produces a steady northward flow of surface air, veering to the westward because of the Coriolis force. A relatively weak ocean current moves westward about the continent. This westward current together with the wind causes the pack ice drift to be predominantly in a direction somewhat to the west of north. This ice drift is a diverging flow since the ice is being moved towards an ever-increasing area of the oceans, in contrast to the essentially bounded movements of the Arctic pack. Consequently the pack is "open" with frequent wide leads and channels between the floes. If it were not for this fortunate fact, marine navigation to Antarctica would be completely impossible instead of merely extraordinarily difficult.

When the drifting ice reaches 50 to 60° South it encounters the great region of the "Westerlies", the great river of air sweeping from west to east between about 40 and 60° South latitude. This is also the region of the Antarctic Convergence where the cold polar water meets the warmer water of temperate oceans. Some of the more polite names given by mariners to this region of the earth are the Roaring Forties and the Screaming Sixties; these are the stormiest seas in the world. Further northward motion of the pack ice is slowed down and hindered by the strong westerly winds, so that this is a region of convergence of ice and the northern boundary of the pack tends to be closely packed and very difficult to traverse by ship. It is not strange that so little was known about the Antarctic continent before the I.G.Y.

3.3 Icebergs

Icebergs are found of almost any shape or size but, at least in northern waters, a typical large berg may be 200 m across and float with some 25 m maximum elevation above the sea. Since about 90 % of its mass is below the surface the depth below the water line would be about 225 m and the total mass might well be as great as 5×10^9 kg, making it a formidable danger to shipping. Barnes (1928, p. 344) showed that water temperature may actually rise very slightly within a few kilometres of an iceberg, and that water temperature is *not* a good indicator of the presence of icebergs. Radar reflections from icebergs are rather uncertain since they offer a small cross-section to electromagnetic waves and reflections are easily lost in wave "clutter", and the best warning is undoubtedly from an underwater sound detection system such as sonar. The *USS Seadragon* had no difficulty in detecting and avoiding icebergs in Davis Strait and the North Atlantic in her 1960 cruise.

Icebergs move under the influence of the same forces listed in section 3.1, but the effect of current is the dominant one. In the case of a floe the lateral extent is so much greater than the thickness that the force exerted by the current against the vertical side of the floe is negligible compared to the water drag on the bottom surface. This is clearly not the case with icebergs. Their great depths provide a large vertical area for the water to push against and icebergs drift almost completely under the control of ocean currents.

Icebergs are virtually non-existent in the Arctic Ocean. (The ice islands discussed in sections 1.4 and 3.1 are much larger and are not usually classed as icebergs.) Their great spawning ground is the coast of Greenland, both east and west, at places where the glaciers of the Greenland Ice Cap flow slowly into the sea. A few icebergs also originate from glaciers on Baffin, Devon, and Ellesmere Islands. The East Greenland Current and lesser, southward currents in Baffin Bay and Davis Strait eventually move most of these icebergs south of Greenland into the Atlantic. The Labrador current which runs southeast helps carry icebergs into the shipping lanes to the northeast of Newfoundland. Since 1913 an International Ice Patrol has kept watch for icebergs in the North Atlantic and issued warnings to shipping. The most dangerous season is March to July and an average of some 300 icebergs of significant size reach areas south of Newfoundland per year.

Compared to the Arctic, everything in the Antarctic seems to be on a large scale, including the icebergs. Some of the tabular bergs are over 500 m thick and several tens of kilometres in width. Their motion northward is similar to the Antarctic pack ice, but they can move right through the region of the Westerlies, on very irregular courses, and penetrate far into the South Pacific and South Atlantic, particularly the latter. Since one of these vast icebergs may take up to 10 years to melt, it can travel great distances under the influence of ocean currents. Icebergs are rarely found north of 40° South, but there are recorded cases of icebergs from Antarctica being sighted in the Tropical Zone.

Glaciers are far from homogeneous, and similarly their offspring, the icebergs, may have flaws and cracks. As an iceberg melts it may split, and the altered distribution of mass may cause it to overturn. Because of its inertia, the motion is ponderous but nevertheless dangerous, and the wisest course is to give icebergs a wide berth.

CHAPTER 4

Ice Control

SECTION 1.5 listed the handful of useful applications of ice, but mostly it is a dangerous nuisance and most ice engineering has to do with its removal. Until recently ice was simply accepted as one of the tribulations of winter, which would go away in the spring of its own accord, but in this century mankind has made greater efforts than ever before to modify his natural environment and to make it suit his purposes better, and this has involved "doing something" about ice. The stimulus came with the automobile and the aeroplane, two devices which work very badly in the presence of too much snow and ice. Large sums of money are spent ploughing the snow from city streets and highways, and the use of chemicals to melt the residual ice is also widespread.

4.1 Chemical Melting and the Use of Heat

The discussion of section 2.2 on the phase diagram of a binary system of a salt and water solution gives all the basic theory behind the use of inorganic salts in melting snow and ice. Provided the air temperature is higher than the eutectic point, $-21 \cdot 1°C$, if solid sodium chloride is sprinkled on ice it will dissolve some of the ice, the exact amount going into solution being calculable from Fig. 4 for any particular air temperature. The resulting brine then drains off a suitably crowned road, which can be freed of ice or snow by the use of sufficient salt. Clearly sodium chloride is useless for this purpose below $-21°C$, and of little value at temperatures near the eutectic temperature because it dissolves such small quantities of ice, and hence for lower temperatures calcium chloride is used.

For reasons of cost, sodium chloride and calcium chloride are the only salts which have been used extensively in de-icing roads, although any salt would be useful above its eutectic point. The disadvantage of this method of treatment is the corrosion of vehicles which results. Brines containing the chloride ion are quite corrosive and the motorist who is most insistent of having bare roads throughout the year is often the first to complain when his car shows spots of rust after two or three winters. This is a very serious problem; where chemical de-icing is used, car bodies are usually badly deteriorated long before the mechanical parts of the vehicle are worn out. Various attempts to overcome the problem have been tried, with limited success so far.

One method is to use a corrosion inhibitor. It is known that certain chromates and permanganates when dissolved in chloride brines reduce considerably the corrosive qualities of these brines. The quantity of inhibitor needed is small, but it must be mixed very intimately with the chloride if it is to be effective. This is easy to do in solution but is a difficult result to achieve with dry materials. Partly for this reason and partly because of cost, no large-scale use of corrosion inhibitors has been tried.

A search has been made for a chemical de-icer which would be relatively cheap, and non-corrosive without an inhibitor. This latter requirement almost forces one to turn to organic materials. Water-soluble organic materials usually have phase diagrams similar to Fig. 4, but since they do not normally ionize in solution they are less effective in depressing the freezing point and the eutectic temperature is not very low. The only suitable, cheap chemical found so far is urea, NH_2CONH_2. Its eutectic temperature is about $-14°C$. Weight for weight it is less than half as effective as calcium chloride in melting ice at $-5°C$. It is virtually non-corrosive to metals, but unfortunately attacks concrete and asphalt slightly, causing spallation and pitting. The desirability of transferring the corrosion from the car to the road is a subject on which motorists and road departments can argue.

The best approach seems to be to design the car better, and automobile manufacturers are giving more thought and effort to combating corrosion by the use of better rust-inhibiting paints, by reducing the number of metals used (dissimilar metals in contact, and wet by brine, tend to set up small electrolytic currents which are remarkably effective in producing corrosion), and by designing the undersurface of the car so that brine can drain off it freely and not collect in partially enclosed cavities.

Ice can affect aircraft adversely in a number of ways. The most obvious danger is ice on the runways, which makes taxiing, take-off, and landing hazardous. Landing is particularly dangerous since high-speed aircraft need long runways to slow down and often rely on mechanical braking of the wheels, although the use of pitch reversal on propeller-driven aircraft and thrust deflection on jets to provide reverse thrust after landing have helped reduce landing runs. Corrosion of aircraft cannot be tolerated so that most inorganic de-icing chemicals are useless. The best present technique is to keep the runways as clear as possible by ploughing and brushing. Then if some ice does form it is covered with an abrasive such as sand to provide a suitably rough surface. To prevent the sand blowing away, it may be applied hot or cemented into place by spraying it with a little water.

When cold, moist air is drawn into a carburettor, there is a danger of ice forming and blocking the fuel jets. This carburettor icing is watched for closely by pilots and can be avoided in a routine way by applying heat to the intake manifold when necessary. A somewhat similar problem exists with the turbine engines used in jets and turboprop aircraft. If ice forms at the air intake it may build up into sizeable pieces which would damage the engine when they released and blew back through the turbine blades. Pulsed electrical heating of the intake regions is used to ensure that any ice which forms is released while it is still too light and thin to cause any damage. The greatest danger from ice is when it forms on the leading edge of the wing and propellers (if any). Occasionally, all too frequently in some locations and seasons, the air contains many fine droplets of supercooled water. When these strike an aircraft they freeze instantly and usually bond strongly to the surface. The rate of ice accretion can be large; in extreme conditions 2 or 3 cm of ice can build up on the leading edge in 5 min. Serious icing normally only occurs for air temperature between 0 and −10°C. It is not the weight of ice which is dangerous, it is the fact that the ice changes the shape of the airfoil and so reduces the lift of the wing or the efficiency of the propeller. Ice can usually be removed from propellers if a little ethyl alcohol is sprayed out of the hub on to the blades at the first sign of ice formation. Since ethyl alcohol has a low freezing point (−115°C) and is completely miscible with water, it will dissolve ice. On the propeller it attacks the bond between the ice and the metal allowing the rotating blades to throw off the ice.

Good methods of wing de-icing have been sought almost since the aircraft was invented, and many different approaches have been tried. Innumerable ice-phobic coatings, pastes, liquids, and paints have been applied to aircraft wings with singularly little success. If the coating is soft enough to be effective, the ice strips it off the wing in a very short time; if the coating is hard enough to last, it does little to prevent ice accretion. Some older aircraft have a so-called rubber "boot" in the leading edge. This is a strip of rubber, fitting smoothly around the front part of the air-foil, which can be flexed mechanically (by air lines) to break off the ice as it forms. This method was abandoned with the newer, faster aircraft because the high-speed airfoils have a very thin, sharply curved leading edge and a rubber boot would be im-practical. Most of these aircraft rely on heat to prevent icing. The leading edge of the wing is built with a double metal skin and provision is made to divert hot air, derived through a heat ex-changer from the turbine exhausts, to pass between these two layers of metal, when icing threatens. The leading edge of the tailplane is usually heated electrically. Despite these precautions, meteorologists and pilots pay very close attention to atmospheric conditions conducive to icing, and every effort is made to limit the length of time spent flying through a region where icing is occurring.

Snow and ice on the wings of an aircraft on the ground can be very dangerous if an attempt is made to take-off without a thorough cleaning of the wings. After brushing off snow, ice can be removed by washing the wing with ethyl alcohol or ethylene glycol. An extremely efficient, if somewhat expensive, de-icing solution can be made up from lithium chloride with potassium chromate as a corrosion inhibitor. This solution is more efficient than calcium chloride in melting ice and so remarkably free of corrosive qualities that it can be applied safely to aircraft. The exact formula, on which the U.S. Navy holds a patent, is given in the July 15, 1957 issue (p. 54) of *American Aviation*. When aircraft must be parked outside overnight, canvas wing covers are often used.

Radiation Heating

The albedo of freshly fallen snow may be as high as 90% and any snow surface which is not too dirty will have an albedo of 65% or more. The solar energy reflected could be put to use melting snow and ice if it could be retained. This can be done, in part at least, by spreading over the snow surface some dark material like soot, cinders, sand, etc. Evidently if this is to be done on a substantial scale some cheap, locally available material must be used. The technique depends on the strength of solar radiation so that it becomes more useful as spring approaches.

One can readily think of various applications for this method of using the available energy of the sun, but the most important uses so far have applied to rivers. In Siberia a number of large rivers (such as the Lena, the Ob, and Yenisei) flow north into the various Arctic seas. These rivers are important means of transport and communication to the Russians who are anxious to open them to navigation as soon as possible in the summer. Long after the seas are passable to ships and the upper reaches of the rivers are open, the river mouths and harbours remain blocked with ice. The Russians have experimented with scattering dark coloured substances on the ice from aircraft, and have found that it is possible to advance the opening of navigation by 2 or 3 weeks.

Another application is in flood control. Rivers which drain an area with considerable snowfall often rise quite sharply in spring, particularly if the area has very little forest cover. Much of Southern Ontario falls into this category and spring flooding is an annual trouble. It can be aggravated if the open river discharges into a bay or lake which is still ice covered. Under certain circumstances some relief from the flooding can be obtained by breaking up the ice cover near the river outlet with this technique of low albedo material. A classic case is described in Barnes (1928, p. 175).

4.2 Icebreakers

The icebreaker is the brute force approach to making a channel in unwanted ice. Icebreakers are costly vessels, both to build and to operate, but their use is often the only method of dealing with ice situations which offer danger to human life and property, or threaten serious economic loss. We may perhaps classify the use of icebreakers under the headings of flood control, aid to winter navigation in temperate regions, and access to far northern and southern waters for scientific and military purposes, although these categories frequently overlap.

Any river system, but particularly one which flows northward so that the ice of its upper reaches breaks loose before its mouth is clear, can present a flood danger from ice. When floating ice moving down river encounters obstacles in the form of shallow or tortuous channels or shorefast ice, ice jams form readily. These jams will impede the flow of water or, in extreme cases, by reaching down to the bottom of the channel may almost totally block the flow, resulting in a rapid rise of the water level upstream. Ice jams are difficult to remove once formed and icebreakers may be used to try to keep a clear channel in which ice may move freely.

The St Lawrence River may be cited again as an example. Just above Montreal there are extensive rapids which normally remain open throughout the winter. Below these rapids the ice cover is rarely continuous across the river and there is usually a large quantity of freely floating ice being carried with the current.

The rapids increase the flooding danger by being prolific generators of frazil ice. Great quantities of this ice are formed in any open water exposed to low air temperatures. At places where the current lessens the frazil floats upward adhering tenaciously to the underside of the ice cover. Great hanging dams of frazil may form in this way. Between Montreal and Lac St Pierre the river is broad and shallow, and broken up with frequent islands. Conditions are ideal for the formation of ice jams, and because the river banks are low and flat this area has a long history of disastrous floods in winter and spring. To lessen the danger, icebreakers now work the river continuously between Quebec City and Montreal from January on, and endeavour to keep ice jams from forming.

When economic conditions warrant, icebreakers may be used to assist navigation throughout the winter season, or to shorten the period when ports must be closed down. Reference has already been made to convoying of merchant ships in winter across the Gulf of St Lawrence. Similar activities go on throughout most of the winter in the Baltic Sea, and farther north the Russians maintain navigation for several months in summer along the Northern Sea Route. The movement of a shipping convoy through heavy ice, when the water is nine-tenths to ten-tenths covered, calls for seamanship of a high order, particularly on the part of the master of the icebreaker. The icebreaker moving through the closely packed ice makes only a temporary channel which may close in a matter of minutes. Hence the vessels of the convoy must follow the icebreaker and each other at very short intervals, maintaining station accurately. If one of the vessels becomes beset by ice so that it cannot move, the icebreaker must go back and "cut it out" of the ice, that is break up the ice around it. Since the icebreaker must move at a fair speed, say 6 or 7 knots, to maintain its way through the ice, and must pass within 30 ft or so of the beset ship if it is to break it free effectively, it is apparent that running a convoy through ice is no job for an inexperienced master.

Since 1945 there has been a great increase in activity in the

Arctic and Antarctic regions, with the installation of numerous weather stations and other scientific establishments, and the construction of radar lines and military bases. Some of the supplies for the construction and maintenance of these sites have of necessity been transported by aircraft, but sea transport is used to the extent practical. Icebreakers have penetrated to very high latitudes and considerable success has also been achieved with ice-strengthened ships, particularly the *Dan* class operated by the Lauritsen Lines of Denmark. These vessels have heavier plating than normal merchantmen, although much lighter than ice-breakers, and a stronger rib structure with a hull shape somewhat like an icebreaker's.

Description of an Icebreaker

There is considerable variety in the size and design of ice-breakers, but some detail on a particular ship will illustrate the properties of this type of vessel. The Canadian icebreaker *CCGS Labrador* (see Fig. 13), belongs to the same class as the American *Wind* ships, although slightly modified in design. She is a vessel of 6000 tons, 269 ft long, with a draft of 31 ft. Propulsion is by two screws aft, driven by a diesel–electric system capable of developing 10,000 h.p., and of driving the ship at 16 knots. To provide ready manœuvrability, the ship is bridge controlled, that is the deck officer in charge has direct control over both steering and propulsion. The bow is narrow and sharply raked to provide a good cutting edge. The hull shape below the waterline is very rounded so that if the ship is trapped in a converging ice area, the pressure will tend to lift the vessel without punching in the sides. This hull shape is very poor in heavy seas so that the vessel rolls wildly in a storm in open water. To offset this, she has Denny-Brown stabilizers, retractable hydrofoils which can be extended outside the hull. These fins are gyroscopically controlled so that they tend to correct automatically for any roll. The principle is the same as that of ailerons on an aircraft. The stabilizers must be retracted within the hull when there is danger of encountering ice.

FIG. 13. The *Canadian Coast Guard Ship Labrador* (in foreground), an icebreaker of 6000 tons displacement, assisting a freighter out of harbour. (*Photograph courtesy of National Film Board of Canada.*)

To resist ice damage, the part of the hull which may come in contact with ice is made of $1\frac{5}{8}$ in. steel plates. A feature peculiar to icebreakers is the system of heeling tanks. In the *Labrador* these consist of three sets of tanks placed symmetrically on the port and starboard sides of the hull. Each tank can contain about 60 tons of salt water. If the three tanks on one side are full and the others empty, the ship lists about 9°. Powerful pumps can transfer the water from the heeling tanks on one side of the ship to those on the other in less than 2 min. Thus the vessel can be rolled through 18° in this time. If this heeling action is carried out with the ship's engines running full astern, it is extremely effective in freeing the ship when she has run up on the ice and become stuck. At one time, the ship had similar tanks which could alter the fore-and-aft trim slightly, but their use has been abandoned as it proved an ineffective method of freeing the ship.

Labrador has a small flight deck and hangar aft, and in Arctic operations carries two Bell Ranger helicopters. Helicopters are essential to a ship trying to move through heavy ice. The route followed is usually tortuous, every effort being made to take advantage of leads and lines of weakness in the ice, which can be spotted far better from the air than from bridge height.

The ship has a crew of ninety-three, carries very large quantities of fuel, and a considerable amount of special equipment for salvage operation, scientific work, etc. As a measure of how specialized the vessel is, there is space for less than 50 tons of general cargo.

The *Labrador* is a typical medium-sized icebreaker. There are a number of considerably large ones in use or under construction, including the Canadian *Macdonald*, the American *Glacier*, and the Russian *Lenin*. The *Lenin* is particularly interesting because it is the only nuclear powered icebreaker in operation; in fact, it was the first surface vessel with this type of power plant. Nuclear power has several advantages for icebreakers. It allows long periods of operation without refuelling, which is very useful in a ship operating in remote regions such as the Arctic. The *Lenin* has an endurance of a year, as compared with some 40 to 50 days for a diesel–electric icebreaker even with its large fuel load. Closely connected with the question of fuel is the ratio of shaft power to displacement, which is sometimes considered to be a figure of merit for icebreakers. For the *Labrador* this "power ratio" is 1·6, for the *Lenin* it is 2·8. The *Lenin* is a large ship, 440 ft (134 m) long with a displacement of 16,000 tons. It has three nuclear reactors, one of which is on standby at any time. Two of the reactors, generating steam for a turbo-electric system, can produce a shaft power of 44,000 h.p. The *Lenin* has disadvantages as well. The turbo-electric propulsion system cannot be controlled as quickly as a diesel–electric system so that the *Lenin* is considerably less manœuvrable than a ship like the *Labrador*. It is interesting to note that the Russians have also built two very large icebreakers, the *Moskva* and the *Leningrad* (26,000 h.p.), of a more conventional type.

Operation of an Icebreaker

An icebreaker such as the *Labrador* can maintain a steady forward speed of several knots through continuous ice of some thickness. Ice is so variable in its strength that an exact figure is impossible, but a thickness of 3 ft of annual sea ice is of the right order. (The *Lenin* is reported to be able to maintain way through over twice this thickness.) At a steady speed, the bow cuts or breaks the ice, producing a crack which runs several feet ahead of the actual point of contact. As the ship moves through the ice the broadening, curved hull section pushes downward on the ice on either side of the crack, breaking off large cakes of ice which are stood on edge and pushed back by the hull. These cakes of ice close in behind the stern so that back of the icebreaker there is channel, of width slightly greater than that of the ship, filled with floating pieces of ice. If the ice cover is not continuous, so that there are some leads or open water patches, icebreaking is considerably easier because there is some place to push the ice broken off floes, and the channel cleared by the ship remains open for a considerably longer time.

When the icebreaker encounters heavier ice, its forward speed will be reduced. The hull is so shaped that the ship tends to ride up on the ice, using its weight to break the heavy, thick cover. If the ice is sufficiently heavy, the icebreaker may be brought to a complete standstill despite the application of full power forward. Then it is necessary to back off and take another run at the barrier. Sometimes the ship will run so far up on the ice that full power astern will not extricate it. The heeling technique described earlier is very useful under these circumstances. As a last resort in very heavy, rafted ice, the icebreaker is sometimes backed slowly into the ice barrier so that the propellers may chop the ice to pieces. This technique is rather hard on propeller blades, but may be necessary at critical places like the entrance to a harbour.

The total thickness of ice through which an icebreaker can make its way depends on the state of the ice (degree of rafting, amount of open water, etc.), the type of ice, and the temperature. As mentioned earlier, it is a safe rule that no attempt should be made to break a polar floe. At air temperatures above $-15°C$ a medium-sized icebreaker can usually get through 6 ft of annual sea ice. Fresh-water ice is harder to break than sea ice at the winter temperatures encountered in temperate latitudes.

4.3   Air Bubbling

The use of air bubbling for ice control is not really new. The *Compressed Air Magazine* for January 1923 contained an article describing an installation in 1917 which was used to protect spillway gates in a dam on the Mississippi River, and there is no reason to believe that this was the first application. However, the technique was largely forgotten until the 1950's when it was "rediscovered" and promoted by Atlas Copco AB of Stockholm. The use of air bubbling is becoming more widespread each year.

Consider first an ideal situation. There is some need to prevent ice formation, or to melt existing ice, in a restricted area of a fresh-water lake. It may be that a wharf is endangered by ice thrust in winter. Suppose the water is 30 ft deep and that the thermocline (see section 1.3) only reaches a maximum depth of 25 ft during the winter. Before freeze-up, polyethylene plastic pipe is laid near the bottom of the lake, being anchored so that it floats just above the bottom in clear water. The pipe should run the full length of the area to be kept open, and if the width is appreciable several parallel lines spaced about 30 ft apart will be needed. These lines are connected to an air compressor. Before laying the pipe a series of small holes about $\frac{1}{16}$ in. in diameter are drilled, with a spacing between holes of 10 ft. When ice threatens, the compressor is turned on and maintains a pressure of about 35 to 40 p.s.i. in the lines, i.e. a minimum pressure differential with the water of 5 to 10 p.s.i. If the system is turned on before any ice forms, an open water pool somewhat larger than the area covered by the pipes will be maintained throughout the winter. If it is not turned on until 2 ft of ice has formed, the ice over the pipes will melt in approximately 4 to 5 days and open water will persist as long as the compressor runs.

The efficacy of an air bubbling system is almost magical to watch, but the explanation of its action in fresh water is simple. It will be recalled that below the thermocline the water temperature is 4°C. As the air bubbles emerge from the orifice in the pipe some of this "warm" water is entrained with the bubbles and transported to the surface. The air bubbler system thus sets up an artificial vertical circulation which brings warmer, bottom water up to the top. The heat capacity of water is very high, 1 ft³ of water at 4°C will melt 86 in³ of ice, in being itself cooled to 0°C. Heat losses from the open water will be considerably greater than if it were ice covered. The bubbler system draws energy from the heat stored in the levels below the thermocline and so increases its depth. This supply is not inexhaustable, but bubbler systems usually draw only slightly on it since the area of the pool or channel kept ice free is small. Incidentally, the power being supplied directly by the compressor is completely trivial in comparison with the power being drawn from the reserve heat of the lake.

The situation described above is an ideal one for good bubbler action, but the surprising thing is how well air bubbling systems work under much less favourable conditions such as shallow or turbulent water. In fact, if there is as little as 0·5C deg. difference in temperature between the level of the bubbler pipe and the surface of the water, useful ice control measures are obtained with such a system. The figures given for the size and spacing of the orifices, for the air pressure in the lines, and for the spacing of the lines are typical of present practice, but none of these factors is at all critical. The rule of thumb that parallel lines should be spaced at a distance equal to the depth of the lines seems to work well. Air bubbling has been used for a variety of purposes: to protect docks from ice damage, and to allow their use in winter, to permit winter construction work on bridge piers, to provide open water so that oxygen may dissolve in a lake for the preservation of fish, to maintain short ferry channels, and so on.

Several experiments have been made in attempts to improve on the bubbler system or to substitute another system for it. One innovation is the installation of stack pipes reaching from slightly above the orifice to just below the surface. The object is to ensure that the "warm" water reaches the surface without mixing in water at intermediate temperatures. Another variation uses a valve so that the air is released in very large bubbles at regular intervals, the so-called "burper" system. Propellers have been mounted under water to produce a steady vertical flow. None of these systems shows much promise. The improvement in performance over a simple, perforated-pipe system is marginal, at best, and the mechanical complexities are considerably greater.

Recalling the discussion of vertical circulation in sea water (section 1.3), the topmost layers of the oceans (down to 100 m or more) are usually isothermal in winter, and any thermoclines are quite deep. It would appear, therefore, that air bubbling would be useless in sea water. Nevertheless, installations have been made (at Thule in Greenland, at Port Cartier on the Gulf of St Lawrence, and at Tuktoyaktuk in the Canadian Arctic), and some success has been achieved in keeping open water for greater or smaller periods of time. It is also significant that other bubbler installations in salt water have been quite ineffective. No satisfactory explanation of the action of a bubbler system in melting sea ice is known. If a salinity gradient exists with more saline water at lower levels, mixing of the water will increase the surface salinity, allowing some ice to be melted, although the quantity is small. It has also been suggested that the induced circulation tends to break up sea ice by erosion of the soft undersurface.

A number of case histories and several technical papers on this subject may be found in *Air Bubbling* (1961).

4.4 Explosives

The use of explosives to break up ice jams, to blast holes in an ice cover or to blow up icebergs is obvious, and needs little discussion. One point of importance may be noted however. Ice is a brittle material, at least for high stress rates, and most of the energy in the detonation of a charge of high explosive in ice is wasted in shattering a small volume of ice into many small fragments. If the object is to disturb a large volume of ice and set it in motion, as in trying to break a jam, the slower burning the explosive the better. The late Howard Barnes developed much experience in dealing with problems of ice control, and was a great believer in the use of thermit, a mixture of powdered aluminium and ferric oxide which can be detonated electrically and which is probably the slowest explosive known. His book, which has been cited already (Barnes, 1928), contains accounts of a number of ice jams broken up with thermit. For some reason its use seems to have gone out of fashion.

CHAPTER 5

The Crystallography of Ice

THE structure of water in all its phases has interested scientists for hundreds of years. Its chemical formula is so simple that it is surprising that an understanding of the arrangements of atoms and molecules in water vapour, liquid water, and ice has been so difficult to achieve, and in fact is far from complete at present. Briefly, we know how two hydrogen atoms and one oxygen atom combine to form a molecule of water vapour. We understand the forces holding them together, and know accurately the angle between the two "arms" of the molecule, the two O—H bonds. Within the last decade the basic structure of ice seems to have been settled finally, although some details remain obscure. The liquid state is the least understood, and this is a general situation in physics, applying to most other substances as well as to water.

The study of ice has long occupied a central place in mineralogy and crystallography. Initially, the classic technique of observing the form of crystals and attempting to deduce the submicroscopic structure was followed. Because of the bewildering variety of forms of solid H_2O, particularly in snow flakes, about the only firm conclusion was that the substructure must contain a hexagonal unit of some type since this structure appears on a macroscopic scale in most snow crystals. Among the more powerful techniques later applied to this problem were spectroscopy, both optical and Raman, diffraction experiments with X-rays, neutrons, and electrons, and precision calorimetry. The discussion of this chapter will necessarily be dogmatic since detailed reports on all of these techniques would be inordinately long. It is hoped that the references given will be adequate to allow anyone interested to follow up the various lines of approach and to see how the conclusions stated here are justified. One of the best general references for this and other aspects of ice is the major work of Shumskii (1955), Part I.

The discussion of ice in this chapter will refer entirely to ice-I, the familiar hexagonal form. At lower temperatures, ice can exist in two other stable forms, below $-70°C$ as a cubic crystal similar to that of diamond, and at still lower temperatures in an amorphous form with no traces of crystal structure. These forms and the various high pressure ices (whose crystal structure is virtually unknown) discovered by Tammann and Bridgman will not be considered.

5.1. The Structure of Water Vapour and Liquid Water

The forces which cause atoms to combine into molecules and ultimately into liquid and solid aggregations originate in the internal structures of the atoms. It is well known that this subatomic domain obeys quite different laws than does matter on a macroscopic scale, and that quantum mechanics must be employed instead of classical physics. In its present state, the mathematical complexities of quantum mechanics are too great to permit exact solutions of any but the simplest problems, but the theory can give qualitative explanations and insights into situations which appeared paradoxical or inexplicable when viewed classically. Our principal interest is in the nature of the bonding forces. Coulson's (1961) treatment will serve as an excellent antidote, if desired, to the somewhat over-simplified discussion below.

A neutral atom consists of a small, heavy nucleus which is positively charged, surrounded by a distribution of negative electrons. The natural unit of electricity is the charge of the electron, $-e$, or that of the proton, $+e$ ($e = 1·60 \times 10^{-19}$ coulombs). The atomic number Z of an atom gives the nuclear charge, Ze, and is also the ordinal number of the element in the periodic table ($Z = 1$ for H, 8 for O, etc.). According to the Heisenberg Uncertainty Principle of quantum mechanics it is impossible to know precisely where the electrons are in an atom, but on the average they are arranged in approximately spherical shells, the K-shell being closest to the nucleus with the L, M, N, etc., shells being at increasing distances. The maximum number of electrons in each shell is very strongly fixed, the K-shell being "closed" when it contains two electrons, the L-shell when it has eight, and so on. The atoms with closed shells are the inert gases helium ($Z = 2$), neon ($Z = 10$), and so on, and their (virtually) complete inability to form chemical compounds shows how stable a structure this closed electron shell is. Rearrangement of electrons to form closed shells is the basis of most chemical combination.

The simplest case is the formation of an alkali halide, potassium chloride for example. Potassium ($Z = 19$) has an electronic structure very similar to the inert gas argon ($Z = 18$) plus one electron in the N-shell. This lone valence electron is physically far removed from the rest of the atom (most of the time) and can be very easily detached. If this is done the atom is said to be ionized into the positive potassium ion K^+ and a free electron e^-. Chlorine ($Z = 17$) also has an electronic structure very similar to that of argon, except that it has one fewer electron, that is it is missing one electron from its outermost shell. The Cl^- ion, which has the same closed shell structure of electrons as argon, is actually more stable than a neutral chlorine atom. If neutral potassium and chlorine atoms are brought close together there is an excellent chance that the valence electron will be transferred from the potassium atom to the chlorine atom, leaving two ions of closed shell structure. The electrostatic attraction between the K^+ and Cl^- ions then holds them together at a distance controlled by the strong, repulsive force which comes into play if two closed shells come near to each other, since closer approach would mean forcing more than the maximum number of electrons into a shell. This type of bond, exemplified by potassium chloride, is called an *ionic bond*. To repeat, the binding force is electrostatic and the equilibrium separation of the ions is determined by the quantum mechanical repulsion of closed shells.

A different type of bond is needed to explain the formation of the hydrogen molecule. Electrostatic attraction plays a negligible part in the binding of this molecule, although there is a weak electrostatic force of attraction, called a van der Waals' force, between hydrogen atoms which helps bring them together. The stability of the molecule depends on a sharing of the two electrons by the two protons which constitute the hydrogen nuclei. Each nucleus thus has a "share" in a closed K-shell. This type of bond is referred to as *covalent*, or homopolar.

Most chemical bonds are intermediate between these two extreme types, and arise from the transfer of one or more electrons part way along the lines joining the atoms in the molecule. Oxygen with eight electrons has a filled K-shell and six electrons in the L-shell, two short of completion. It thus has an electron affinity of two which can be satisfied by combining with two hydrogen atoms to form a water molecule. The binding forces are principally of the covalent type.

The structure of the water molecule has been deduced from a large number of chemical and physical experiments which can be discussed only sketchily here. A symmetrical linear molecule is ruled out immediately because water is a polar molecule with a permanent electric dipole moment. Debye (1929, pp. 63–76) showed that an asymmetric linear molecule of water (different O—H separations) would be unstable, as would be an asymmetric triangular one. Thus H_2O has the form of an isosceles triangle. The quantum mechanical theory of this molecule (see Mott and Sneddon, 1948, Chapter VII) shows that the angle between the two O—H bonds must be slightly greater than $90°$ but the theory is, as yet, unable to predict the angle or interatomic distances precisely.

Because of its shape the H_2O molecule will have three different moments of inertia (for rotation about an axis perpendicular to the plane of the molecule, for rotation about an O—H line, and for rotation about the H—H line). These moments of inertia determine some of the spectral frequencies of water vapour, infrared rotational, rotation–vibration, Raman, etc., and in principle measurements of the various spectra permit the deduction of the moments of inertia and hence of the details of the structure. For further information, see Herzberg (1945, p. 280).

Figure 14 shows the present ideas on the structure of the water vapour molecule. The circles represent the three nuclei and the shaded areas represent approximately the distribution of the "cloud" of ten electrons. An isolated oxygen atom has an electron distribution which is roughly spherical except for two "holes" in the cloud along two axes at right angles to each other. The electrons from the two hydrogen atoms tend to fit into this structure and fill these "holes", which accounts for the angle between the two O—H bonds being roughly 90°. However, this leaves the H^+ ions or protons relatively bare and their mutual repulsion increases the angle between the bonds. The electron cloud is considerably distorted from the oxygen structure by the electrostatic forces. The electron distribution shown is only schematic, but the figures on the angle between bonds (104° 31′) and on the spacing between the oxygen nucleus and either hydrogen nucleus (0·96 Å) are known with some precision.

When water vapour is cooled to liquid water so that the average spacing of the molecules becomes small, an additional force comes into play. The average spacing can be calculated as follows. Assume (for this purpose only) that a water molecule occupies a cube of side l, so that each cube contains the mass of one water molecule. Avogadro's number $N_0 = 6·025 \times 10^{23}$ gives the number of molecules in a gram-molecular weight, which is 18·02 g for water. At 4°C the specific gravity of water is 1·000 to the accuracy we need. Hence

$$l^3 N_0 \, cm^3 = 18·02 \, cm^3; \quad l = 3·10 \times 10^{-8} \, cm = 3·10 \, Å$$

Comparing this figure with the O—H separation of 0·96Å or the H—H separation of 1·52 Å in water, it is clear that the water molecules are very tightly packed indeed. Referring to Fig. 14, it will be noticed that small concentrations of negative charge are shown on the sides of the oxygen opposite to the O—H bonds. If a "bare" H^+ ion of a water molecule comes near one of these charge concentrations on another water molecule there will be a

small electrostatic attraction between them which may be sufficient to bond the two molecules together, temporarily at least.
This linkage is called a *hydrogen bond* or a proton bond. It is by
no means restricted to water, but it is particularly important in the
case of liquid water and especially of ice. Figure 15 shows a

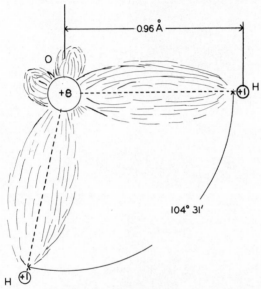

FIG. 14. The structure of the water vapour molecule H_2O. The
shading is intended to represent the approximate distribution of the
electron cloud.

schematic diagram of a dimer of two water molecules combined.
Since the hydrogen atom has a single electron it can form only
one covalent bond, and the hydrogen bond must be almost
entirely ionic in character. In the figure the stronger covalent
bonds are shown by solid lines and the hydrogen bond by a dotted
line.

From Figs. 14 and 15 it might appear that a second hydrogen
bond might form to the upper oxygen atom, but apparently this is
improbable in liquid water; usually a maximum of one hydrogen

bond occurs per oxygen atom. (But see section 5.5 for an exception.) There is nothing to prevent another water molecule becoming attached to the lower oxygen atom, however, and a twisted linear polymer, $(H_2O)_n$, can form in this way. This polymerization or *association* of water is believed to account for the peculiar properties of liquid water. There is no agreement on the

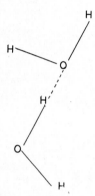

Fig. 15.   Structure of a "dimer" $(H_2O)_2$. The solid lines are covalent bonds and the dotted line is a hydrogen bond.

number n which indicates the number of H_2O units grouped in a single large molecule. Because of the weakness of the hydrogen bond these large molecules cannot be stable, and one must visualize liquid water as consisting of a number of polymerized units of various sizes surrounded by monomers, the large molecules constantly changing in size as hydrogen bonds are broken and reformed because of thermal agitation. One estimate based on neutron diffraction results is that at low temperatures (0–10°C), n averages 5 or 6. The degree of association must diminish with increasing temperature, but there is some evidence from latent heats of evaporation that there is some slight association even in steam, at temperatures just above the boiling point. For discussions of the structure of water, see Frank (1958), Bernal (1958), and Pauling (1960, p. 472).

5.2 Diffraction of X-ray, Neutron, and Electron Beams

The best information on the crystalline structure of ice comes from diffraction experiments with X-rays, neutrons, and electrons. There is a vast literature on the experimental techniques of diffraction studies in crystallography and on the theoretical methods of their interpretation. Bacon (1955) and Clark (1955) are good general references. Results for ice are given in Bacon (1955, p. 166), Barnes (1929), Blackman and Lisgarten (1958), Lonsdale (1958), Owston (1958), and Peterson and Levy (1957).

X-rays are a form of electromagnetic radiation with wavelengths of the order of 0·1 to 3Å. Neutrons and electrons are usually thought of as material "particles", but, according to quantum mechanics, they also behave as if they were waves. The wavelength of a particle depends on its momentum p, according to the de Broglie equation $\lambda = h/p$, where λ is the wavelength and h is Planck's constant $6·625 \times 10^{-34}$ joule-sec. These are de Broglie or matter waves, not electromagnetic ones, but they show similar properties of interference and diffraction. Thermal neutrons, that is neutrons in thermal equilibrium with matter at room temperature, have an energy of about $1/40$ eV and a corresponding wavelength of 1·81Å. Electrons accelerated through a potential difference of 60 V, and therefore with an energy of 60 eV, have a wavelength of 1·58Å.

Crystals are regular arrays of atoms with interatomic spacings of the order of 1 to 5Å. Because of the regularity of the crystal lattice, it will diffract a beam of any of the radiations of the last paragraph, just as a ruled grating will diffract visible light. The rule that diffraction will be significant only when the wavelength of the radiation and the characteristic grating separation are of comparable size is clearly satisfied. When radiation strikes an atom in the lattice it will be scattered in all directions. In any direction making a random angle with the direction of the incident beam the contributions scattered from various atoms will usually have random phase relations, and will cancel each other out. In certain specific directions, however, the phase differences will be coherent and the scattered waves will combine to give a diffracted beam of measurable intensity. The first X-ray diffraction photograph was made in 1913 by allowing a collimated beam of X-rays to pass through a single crystal of zinc blende and fall on a photographic plate. When the plate was developed, an intense central spot caused by undeflected X-rays was found to be surrounded by a complex symmetrical array of diffuse spots corresponding to the directions of constructive interference in the crystal.

The analysis of X-ray diffraction by crystals was simplified by W. L. Bragg. He pointed out that all the atoms of a crystal could be considered to lie on a set of equally spaced parallel planes. Any number of these sets of planes could be drawn, although only a few of the sets would contain any appreciable density of atoms on a plane. Bragg showed that any one of these planes could be considered as a very inefficient mirror which reflected a small part of the incident X-rays according to the usual law of reflection of light. Constructive interference could only occur for directions in which the reflected waves (diffracted, actually) from *all* of a set of Bragg planes were in phase. Figure 16 shows these Bragg criteria for a (mythical) cubic crystal composed of identical atoms, all spaced a distance d apart. Only a vertical section through the crystal is shown. The dotted lines indicate one set of Bragg planes (the most fundamental set for this crystal). A plane wave of monochromatic X-radiation is incident at an angle θ. The direction of propagation of the wave is shown by rays and θ is the angle between a ray and one of the Bragg planes. (Note that θ is the complement of the angle of incidence as defined in optics.) Bragg's rules tells us that we need only look for a diffracted beam along rays such as $A_1 Q_1$ where $P_1 A_1 Q_1$ lie in a plane and $P_1 A_1$ and $A_1 Q_1$ make equal angles with the Bragg plane. The second criterion is that the diffracted waves travelling in the directions $A_1 Q_1$ and $A_2 Q_2$ must be in phase, that is that the path lengths $P_1 A_1 Q_1$, $P_2 A_2 Q_2$ must differ by an integral number of wavelengths $n\lambda$. Dropping perpendiculars $A_1 B$ and $A_1 C$ on $P_2 A_2$ and $A_2 Q_2$, the path difference is $BA_2 + A_2 C = 2BA_2$. From the

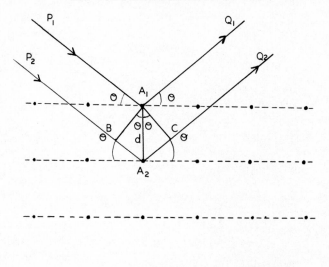

FIG. 16.   Bragg reflections from a simple cubic crystal.

geometry $\angle BA_1A_2 = \theta$ so that $2BA_2 = 2A_1A_2 \sin\theta = 2d \sin\theta$. Hence the directions of diffracted beams are given by the Bragg equation

$$n\lambda = 2d \sin\theta \qquad (4)$$

It is evident that the waves diffracted by the third and deeper Bragg planes will be in phase with those from the first two planes.

Equation (4) is the basis of diffraction studies of crystal structure. The integer n is usually 1, and only very rarely ambiguous. If λ is known and θ is measured we can solve for d, and the size of the unit cell of the crystal is known. No crystal in nature is so obliging as to have a unit cell which is cubic with identical atoms at its corners only, although the alkali halides, particularly potassium chloride, KCl, come close to it. These halides consist of a cubical unit with an alkali ion and a halogen ion located at any two adjacent lattice sites, so that each type of ion has six of the other type as nearest neighbours. In the case of potassium chloride, the K^+ and Cl^- ions each have the same number of electrons and they are almost but not quite identical in their ability to scatter X-rays. If the difference is ignored, potassium chloride is a simple cubic crystal, and Bragg reflection from the principal planes shows that their spacing d is 3.14Å. Thus any two adjacent ions are separated by this distance. A study of the *intensities* of Bragg reflections from different sets of planes establishes that the scattering powers of the two ions differ slightly, and that the ions must alternate in the structure.

To study an unknown crystal one first looks for symmetry lines or planes, if any, in the macroscopic form of the crystal. The crystal is then placed in the X-ray beam and slowly rotated about some axis of symmetry, noting the angles of all the Bragg reflections which are observable, and their relative intensities. This process is repeated for other axes of symmetry, or for a set of three orthogonal axes in any event. The resulting Bragg angles and spacings of the Bragg planes usually permit deduction of the size and shape of the unit cell. The intensity data furnishes information about the crystal structure within the cell, and usually the complete structure and spacings can be found, although deductive analysis of a high order may be needed. The reasons for the difficulty in finding the structure of ice will be discussed in section 5.4.

The theory of neutron and electron diffraction is very similar to that of X-ray diffraction, although the experimental techniques differ considerably. The advantage of having the three methods available is that the various types of radiation are scattered from atoms in different ways. X-rays are scattered almost entirely by the electrons of the atom. The scattering is a complex process, with the intensity of the scattered radiation depending on both the wavelength and the atomic number of the target atoms. For $\lambda > 0.5\text{Å}$, the scattering intensity varies approximately as Z^2 and for the lighter atoms ($Z < 10$) decreases only very slowly as λ decreases. For heavier atoms the scattering coefficient increases somewhat more rapidly with Z than a square-law relation, but, of more importance, the intensity of scattering decreases very rapidly with decrease in λ. The effect of these relations is that X-ray crystallography is quite difficult for a substance containing two kinds of atoms of widely different Z values. This is particularly true if one of the atoms is hydrogen, which is a poor scatterer of X-rays at best.

An electron beam is also scattered by the electrons of an atom, but the interaction is much more intense. For a given target atom, the fraction of an electron beam scattered is of the order of 10^8 times as great as the fraction of an X-ray beam scattered. Because of the large scattering coefficient the penetration of electrons into solid matter is slight, and electron diffraction is most useful for studying the structure of thin films. The scattering coefficient varies approximately as the first power of Z, and electron diffraction can be used to study the position of lighter atoms in a crystal. This is also the great advantage of neutrons. They interact with the nucleus of an atom and the scattering of neutrons by light nuclei is large. The reactions are somewhat complex and there is no simple relationship between the intensity of neutron scattering and either the Z value of the target nucleus or the energy of the neutrons. Unfortunately, the interactions between neutrons and protons are so complex that the coherent scattering we are interested in is obscured by another type called incoherent. For this reason the neutron diffraction studies on ice by Peterson and Levy and earlier workers were carried out on heavy water ice, D_2O, since the unwanted scattering is not found to nearly the same extent in reactions between a neutron and deuteron.

5.3 The Structure of Ice

Barnes (1929) used X-ray methods to study single crystals of ice. His technique gave no information about the positions of the hydrogen atoms but he was able to show that the oxygen atoms are arranged in a tetrahedral pattern, each oxygen atom being surrounded by four (approximately) equally spaced oxygen atoms at the vertices of a tetrahedron. Each pair of oxygen atoms is linked by a hydrogen bond. If the tetrahedron were "perfect", that is if all the bonds were of equal length and all the $O'OO''$

and O″OO″ angles (see Fig. 17) were equal, these interior angles of the tetrahedron would all be 109° 28′. Slight deviations from this figure will be discussed later, but the deviations are small and it is an excellent first approximation to take the oxygen atoms in ice as being arranged in sets of interlocking perfect tetrahedra. Assuming the hydrogen atoms to lie along the bonds, we see that the angle of a water molecule is altered from 104·5° in the vapour phase to 109·5° in the solid phase.

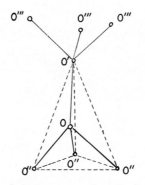

Fig. 17. Sketch of the structure of an ice lattice showing the tetrahedral bond arrangement.

We next show how this tetrahedral arrangement of oxygen atoms in ice leads to the characteristic hexagonal symmetry. Figure 17 shows a sketch of a small section of the lattice. Solid lines represent hydrogen bonds and the outline of the tetrahedron surrounding the oxygen atom marked as O is shown by dashed lines. The three atoms marked O″ form an equilateral triangle in a plane which is called the *basal plane* of the lattice. The O′O bond gives the direction known as the *c*-axis, which is perpendicular to the basal plane. Consider now the four bonds of the atom O′. One of them is the bond O′O and the other three must go to three equally spaced O‴ atoms as shown. These three atoms must also lie in a plane perpendicular to O′O. Thus the tetrahedron about O′ is inverted, with its base parallel to that of the tetrahedron about O. We see how the set of basal planes of the lattice is formed.

In Fig. 17 the complete bond system is shown for the atoms O, O' only, but of course each of the six O″, O‴ atoms must have three additional bonds. Extension of the three-dimensional sketch of Fig. 17 would be complicated, so we turn to Figs. 18 and 19

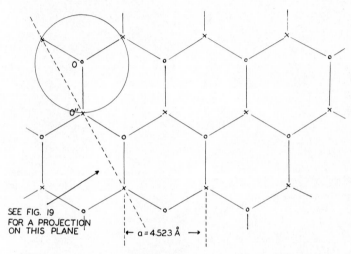

FIG. 18. Projection of the ice lattice on a basal plane. Circles and crosses indicate oxygen atoms on two different planes. Only the "slanting" bonds are shown.

which shows projections of the lattice on the basal plane, and on a plane passing through a c-axis of the crystal. In Fig. 18 the plane of the paper is the basal plane, which we can call horizontal for convenience. Two different planes of atoms are superimposed in the figure, and are distinguished by using circles and crosses. If we consider the direction from O to O' in Fig. 17 as "up" and if we identify one of the circles in Fig. 18 as the atom O of Fig. 17, then the atoms represented by circles are higher than those represented by crosses. With respect to the direction convention we have adopted there are two types of bonds, the OO' type which is vertical and the OO″ type which is slanting. Only the latter are shown in Fig. 18. The atom O in Fig. 18 has one vertical, upward bond, which is not shown, and three downward slanting bonds to three O″ atoms. Turning our attention to the O″ atom marked, it also has one vertical bond (downward) and three upward slanting bonds. One of these is fixed in direction and length to

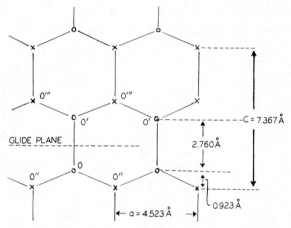

FIG. 19. Projection of the ice lattice on a plane through the c-axis.

the O atom shown. Hence the direction and length of the other two bonds are also fixed, and there must be two oxygen atoms at the locations shown by circles at the ends of these bonds. Since all bond lengths and angles are the same these atoms must line in the same horizontal plane as O.

Proceeding in this way we see that the perfect tetrahedral symmetry assumed requires that all the O atoms be in one plane and all the O″ atoms in another parallel plane a short distance lower down. The figure also shows that the bonds form a repeated pattern of hexagons, hexagons which are not in one plane but zigzag back and forth between the two planes. The size of a hexagon is described in terms of the distance a between parallel sides, as measured on the projection on the basal plane. The cell dimension of 4·523 Å shown on the figure is for H_2O ice at 0°C.

Figure 19 is a projection on a plane, parallel to the c-axis of the crystal, which passes through a pair of O″ atoms. For simplicity the third O″ atom of each set of three is not shown. Circles and crosses in this figure are used to indicate atoms which are in different *vertical* planes, as we shall see. This diagram brings out an important point which is not obvious from the two previous figures. Looking at Fig. 17, one might think that the upper group of three atoms (O‴) could rotate easily about the OO′ axis, or in other words that there might be no relation between the positions of the three O‴ atoms with respect to the three O″ ones. In fact, in a perfect ice crystal each O‴ atom must be vertically above an O″ atom. The lower two layers of atoms in Fig. 19 are the two layers shown in Fig. 18 and their positions are fixed. The bonds upward from atoms such as O must be vertical so that the positions of the O′ atoms are fixed. It remains only to establish the position of O‴. This atom must be linked to three O′ atoms in exactly the same way as each O″ atom is linked to three O atoms. The geometry has only two solutions. The O‴ may lie directly above O″ or it may be over the vacant centre of one of the hexagons of Fig. 18. Ice at normal temperatures has the first of these structures. Diamond is an example of the second, and it has already been pointed out that ice can crystallize in this form at low temperatures. In Fig. 19, then, the fourth row of atoms (O‴) is directly above the bottom row (O″), with the second and third rows (O, O′) also in a vertical plane but set slightly back of the O″O‴ plane. The cell parameter c is the minimum vertical separation in which the pattern repeats exactly.

The cell dimensions given in Fig. 19 again refer to H_2O ice at 0°C. Figures 18 and 19 are drawn to the same scale.

This discussion of the structure of the ice lattice leads immediately to a number of conclusions. First, it is a very open lattice; the spacings between the oxygen atoms are quite large compared with the size of the atoms themselves. Even when the hydrogen atoms are fitted in, there is a great deal of empty space in ice.

It is worth repeating that the cell dimensions given in the figures were determined experimentally; quantum mechanical theory is not quite sufficiently developed for calculation of the cell parameters. From the experimental cell constants we can calculate the density of ice by selecting a representative volume of the ice and counting the number of molecules in this volume. Let us choose as a unit of area one of the hexagons of Fig. 18. If d represents the length of one side of the regular hexagon, simple geometry gives us that

$$d = \frac{a}{2} \sec 30° = \frac{4·523}{2} \times \frac{2}{\sqrt{3}} = 2·611 \text{Å}$$

Hence, area of hexagon $= 6 \times (d/2) \times d \cos 30° = 17·72 \text{Å}^2$.

From Fig. 19, the vertical separation between two of these double layers of oxygen atoms is $2·760 + 0·923 = 3·683$ Å so that our unit of space is a right, hexagonal prism of volume

$$17·72 \times 3·683 = 65·27 \text{Å}^3$$

Now we must count the oxygen atoms in this volume. In the notation of Fig. 19, we may consider that O and O″ atoms are in this volume but O′, O‴ atoms are in the next unit of space above the one we are considering. Hence there are six oxygen atoms in the hexagonal prism but each of these is shared between the three hexagons which meet at each vertex (Fig. 18). The number of oxygen atoms per unit volume is thus one third of six, or two. Each of these must have two hydrogen atoms attached to it, so our unit volume contains two ice molecules. Using Avogadro's number N_0, the volume of a mole of ice is

$$(1/2) \times 6·025 \times 10^{23} \times 65·27 \times 10^{-24} \text{ cm}^3 = 19·66 \text{ cm}^3$$

since $1 \text{Å} = 10^{-8}$ cm. The mass of a mole of ice is $18·02$ g so the density of H_2O ice at $0°C$ is predicted to be

$$\rho = \frac{18·02}{19·66} = 0·9164 \text{ g cm}^{-3}$$

Since the experimental value is usually given as $0·9168$ the agreement is fairly satisfactory.

The next point is that ice has only one important axis of symmetry, the c-axis. The properties of a single crystal of ice may be expected to be isotropic in all directions perpendicular to the c-axis, but some anisotropy is to be expected between properties measured parallel and perpendicular to the c-axis. Comparatively few experiments have been made on single crystals of ice, but they show that the amount of anisotropy varies considerably from one property to another. Butkovich (1957) showed that the coefficient of linear expansion of ice is isotropic in single crystals. On the other hand, there is some evidence that the thermal conductivity of ice is slightly greater along the c-axis than transverse to it (Dorsey, 1940, p. 481), and there is no doubt that the elasticity of single crystals of ice is anisotropic. Stephens (1958) gives a review of the elastic behaviour of ice crystals and of the experimental work on this subject.

Next, let us refer again to Fig. 19 where a "horizontal" plane is indicated and labelled as a *glide plane*, sometimes referred to as a slip plane. If all of the crystal above this plane were displaced horizontally to the right by 4·523 Å, or any integral multiple of this distance, exactly the same structure would result. This, of course, is just what is meant by a cell constant in crystallography, and it is also true that if a portion of the crystal were displaced "vertically" by a distance nc, where n is an integer, the crystal pattern would be unaltered. However, the number of bonds which must be broken to allow a horizontal slip is very much smaller than the number involved in a vertical slip. In fact, the activation energy for vertical slip must be very high because slippage is only observed parallel to the basal planes. This term activation energy needs explanation. If a horizontal displacement of amount na occurs, the final state looks exactly like the initial state, and the potential energy of the crystal is unchanged. However, the motion will not occur spontaneously since the energy required to break the OO' bonds must first be supplied from some external source. When the motion stops this amount of energy has been absorbed by the system as heat, that is the crystal is warmed up slightly by the slippage. This sort of situation is quite common in physics and chemistry. When a system has two possible states and the final state has the same or less energy than the initial one, the transition may occur spontaneously or it may be that some minimum amount of energy must be supplied to start the reaction. The minimum energy is called the activation energy for the reaction.

If a shear stress is applied to a crystal of ice, parallel to the basal plane, a shear strain and resulting slip occur quite readily. It is for this reason that ice displays the plastic properties to be discussed in the next chapter. Plastic flow is most strikingly shown in the motion of glaciers.

Finally, we return to the idea of rotation about the OO' bonds of Fig. 17. Our discussion has shown that in a perfect crystal the oxygen atoms are so interlocked that no such rotation should occur. All actual crystals must have a surface, however, and a surface is a place where the bond structure is not complete. At the surface we must have many places where one, two, or three atoms such as O''' are attached to an O' atom but have formed no other bonds. Such a group could evidently rotate easily and a surface layer of this type would have a mobility and an inability to support shear stress more typical of a liquid than of a solid. There is considerable evidence that ice, even at very low temperatures, is usually covered by a thin liquid-like layer of this type. See Nakaya and Matsumoto (1954).

The modern theory of solids has shown that no crystals of macroscopic size are ever perfect, but must have numerous imperfections or lattice defects. These defects may be simply holes in the lattice where one or more atoms are missing, or lines where parts of the crystal do not fit together correctly, or foreign atoms which have been squeezed into the lattice. Where imperfections exist in an ice crystal there is a possibility of rotation about bonds and it is believed that this occurs occasionally in the interior of an ice crystal, particularly when the temperature approaches the melting point and the amplitudes of thermal vibration become large.

5.4   The Positions of the Hydrogen Atoms

The discussion of the long, preceding section was based entirely on Barnes's (1929) model of the position of the oxygen atoms in ice. Subsequent work has improved the accuracy with which the cell constants are known, but has always confirmed that this model of the structure is correct. The locations of the hydrogen atoms is another matter, which was not really settled until the neutron diffraction studies of Peterson and Levy (1957).

Barnes first suggested tentatively that a hydrogen atom (an ion really) was situated midway between each pair of oxygen atoms. For this to be true it would be necessary for the covalent bond between the H and one of the O's to be of the same strength as the hydrogen bond between the H and the other O atom. Since the hydrogen would belong equally to two oxygens it could no longer be part of a unique water molecule, in fact the entire crystal would have to be considered as one single macromolecule. This sort of structure does occur with the solid alkali halides, as has already been described. Two general objections seemed to rule this structure out for ice. First, ionic crystals usually have a very high melting point (800°C for sodium chloride). Second, and of more weight, this "Barnes" structure is uniquely fixed. For given cell constants the exact mean position of each $O^=$ and H^+ ion is fixed, where the mean positions are the centres of the amplitudes of thermal vibration. Such a system has no zero-point entropy, yet the residual entropy of ice has been measured as 0·82 cal/mole deg. This rather technical point is discussed, with references, along with other anomalies of ice by Giguère (1959) in an interesting review article.

If, then, ice is not an ionic crystal, it must be a molecular one, that is each pair of H atoms belongs specifically to a particular O atom, so that the H atom on any O—O line is closer to one of the O atoms. It seems reasonable to assume that the H_2O molecules in ice are identical, with a constant O—H separation in the molecules. If this is the case, there are six possible arrangements of the hydrogen atoms on the four bonds from each oxygen atom. (See Owston (1958, p. 176) for diagrams of these arrangements.) If any one of these six arrangements predominated, ice would have a permanent dipole moment and would be piezoelectric, properties which it does not appear to have. In 1935 Pauling first suggested that all six possible arrangements of the hydrogen atoms are equally probable, and must occur with equal frequency in ice. In this statistical or half-hydrogen model, the H atom on a given O—O bond will be about 1 Å from either end, but it is impossible to say which position it will occupy. To a neutron beam it will appear that on the average there are *two* hydrogens on each bond, but each will scatter neutrons (or electrons or X-rays) with only half the intensity of a true hydrogen atom. This very unusual structure is confirmed in two ways. Pauling showed that the randomness of positioning of the hydrogens in ice is just that needed to account for the experimental value of the residual entropy. Since all the possible arrangements of H atoms will give crystals of identical potential energy, he proved that a crystal with N molecules can have any of $(3/2)^N$ structures and he then showed that the crystal will therefore have a residual entropy of

$$k \ln(\tfrac{3}{2})^N = R \ln(\tfrac{3}{2}) = 0 \cdot 806 \, \text{cal/mole degree}$$

where k, R are Boltzmann's constant and the universal gas constant. This is in excellent agreement with the experimental figure of $0 \cdot 82$.

The clinching evidence for the Pauling structure came from the neutron diffraction studies of single crystals of D_2O ice at $-50°C$ (see section 5.2 for the reasons governing the choice of heavy ice) by Peterson and Levy. Their results are shown in Fig. 20. All the spacings are in Å, and their standard deviations for distances and angles are omitted for clarity but are given in their paper. The open circles represent the O atoms and the half-solid circles give the possible positions of the deuterium atoms.

Since the hydrogen atoms normally occupy positions about 1 Å from one end or other of the O—O bond and have equal energies in either position this must be because an H^+ ion at the centre of the bond would have a higher energy. This is one of the activation energy situations discussed in the last section. A proton (or deuteron) at one position on a bond, such as D_1 in Fig. 20, may then move to the other position (D_2) if it is supplied the proper activation energy (from thermal agitation or an external electric field) or it may get from D_1 to D_2 by a peculiar quantum mechanical

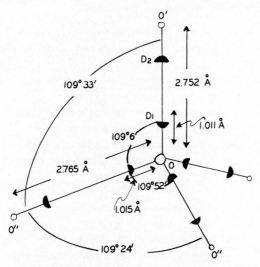

FIG. 20. The dimensions of the D_2O structural unit in ice at $-50°C$. Data of Peterson and Levy (1957).

process called "tunneling" which has no classical analogue. Suppose at some instant the system of Fig. 20 is in its equilibrium state with two deuterons in D_1 positions and two in D_2 positions. If for some reason a deuteron "jumps" from a D_2 position near O' to the D_1 position on this bond, the O atom region acquires an excess positive charge and the O' atom loses positive charge, setting up an electric dipole along the OO' line. The field of this dipole will influence nearby positive charges. One possibility would be a jump from D_1 to D_2 positions along one of the OO'' bonds. Such a jump restores the normal charge distribution near

O but upsets it near O″. In this way a single motion of positive charge may be propagated through the crystal in a series of discrete charge movements. This proton (or deuteron) jump mechanism is thought to be the principal means of electrical conduction through ice.

Deviations from Tetrahedral Symmetry

The numerical values in Fig. 20 show that a D_2O crystal does not have the perfect tetrahedral symmetry discussed in section 5.3. None of the angles is exactly 109° 28′ and the OO″ bonds are significantly longer than the OO′ bond. Similar results (of somewhat less precision) have been obtained with H_2O ice. The three "base" bonds are slightly pushed down from the "perfect" position. These refinements of measurement and the lack of perfect symmetry do not invalidate any of the conclusions of section 5.3. There are indications that the tetrahedra in an ice crystal approach more closely the dimensions of a perfect tetrahedron as the temperature is reduced, so that the deviations must represent adjustments to accommodate increased thermal agitation.

Rather more interesting are the indications in the figure that the deuterons do not lie exactly on the O—O lines. The transverse displacement from a linear bond is extremely small, not more than 0·006 Å from the data, and there is considerable doubt whether the accuracy of the experiment makes this significant. Nevertheless, this is perhaps the final point which needs more experimental clarification in our knowledge of the structure of ice.

5.5　The Density of Ice and Water

We are now in a position to see qualitatively why the density of ice and water vary in such a peculiar fashion near the freezing point. The relatively low density of ice reflects its very open crystal structure, which results from the geometry forced on it by the bonding forces holding it together. All solids expand with increasing temperature (except where an actual phase change from one crystal structure to another occurs) because of the increased amplitude of thermal vibration. In H_2O ice the cell parameter a increases from 4.480Å at $-180°C$ to 4.523Å at $0°C$. When the thermal agitation increases to the point where the crystalline bonds (the hydrogen bonds in the case of ice) can no longer restrain the motion of individual molecules, the crystal structure breaks down, that is, melting occurs. Cold, liquid water, as we have seen, is made up of mixtures of polymerized H_2O molecules including some monomers. These molecules are mostly irregular in shape but nearly linear and so can pack together more closely than do the molecules of ice. Thus when ice melts the density increases.

There is some, not too conclusive evidence from neutron diffraction (Brockhouse, 1958) that water, even at room temperature, contains some ice-like structures, that is that some of the $(H_2O)_n$ molecules are not long chains but group themselves into something resembling the ice lattice. These will act to reduce the mean density because of their open structure. These pseudo ice crystals in the water may be fairly plentiful at low temperatures near the freezing point, but they must become increasingly rare and unstable as the temperature rises. Their breakup into nearly linear molecules will result in a tendency for the density to *increase* with rising temperature. On the other hand, the increasing thermal energy of water molecules will result in expansion with rising temperature, that is a tendency for *decreasing* density. Evidently these opposing trends combine to give the maximum density at $4°C$, the breakup of "ice" crystals being the dominant factor between $0°$ and $4°C$ and the expansion of water becoming more important at temperatures greater than $4°C$.

There is a great deal of evidence, more than we have been able to present, that the qualitative explanation just given is substantially correct, but a quantitative theory of the liquid water state certainly does not exist. A critical test of any such theory will be its ability to predict the correct variation of density with temperature.

CHAPTER 6

The Mechanical Properties of Ice

ICE in its natural state is almost invariably polycrystalline, and the discussion in this chapter will be limited to ice of this type, unless there is a specific reference to measurements on single crystals. Polycrystalline ice usually contains impurities—air bubbles, salts, dirt, organic matter, etc.—which are found both at crystal boundary surfaces and between the platelets of an ice crystal, as discussed in sections 2.4 and 2.6. Furthermore, ice crystals vary widely in size, and often in the orientations of their c-axes. Most natural ice shows some degree of order in these orientations, strongly in the case of ice covers on water, less so in glaciers, and least in ice freshly formed by the compaction of snow. Because of all of these factors the physical properties of ice, particularly the mechanical properties, show a large scatter in observed values, even when samples from nearby parts of a large mass of ice are measured. This scatter results in part from real physical differences between the samples. Experimental inaccuracies, which are often important, also contribute to the observed spread.

In general, then, values of physical parameters representative of a large mass of ice cannot be found from single measurements, and a series of observations, large enough in number to apply statistical techniques, is necessary. Many of the observations reported in the literature are of little value because of insufficient information about the character of the ice and the details of the experimental method employed. Full details are particularly important in the case of sea ice where variations in temperature, salinity, density, and crystal structure and orientation may all affect the values of other physical parameters significantly.

Excellent summaries of data on ice are given in Dorsey (1940), Mantis (1951), and Voitkovskii (1960). Most of these data refer to fresh-water ice. The summaries will not be repeated here and only representative figures for fresh-water ice will be quoted, partly because this type of ice is a limiting case of sea ice. It is usually possible to give a single figure for a physical property of fresh-water ice which is meaningful, but all properties of sea ice should preferably be in the form of equations relating the parameter to the variables of temperature, salinity, and density (whose influence can often be represented by the single combined parameter of brine content v defined in section 2.4) and of crystal size and orientation. These equations can only rarely be given at the present time because of lack of experimental observations.

6.1 The Rheological Nature of Ice

Rheology is the science of the deformation and flow of matter. Ice is a rather complex material from this point of view. Its anisotropy with respect to the c-axis has been referred to repeatedly, but we may neglect this for the present and consider it to be isotropic. Ice is usually described as a visco-elastic solid. Let us discuss the elastic behaviour first. An elastic solid is one which obeys Hooke's law, suffers a deformation or strain proportional to the applied stress or force per unit area, and recovers its original condition completely when the stress is removed.

Three types of stress can be applied. Figure 21 illustrates longitudinal stress. A cylinder of ice, whose unstrained dimensions are shown, is subjected to tension along its axis. The stress σ_X equals T/A, where A is the cross-sectional area of the cylinder. As a result of this stress the length of the cylinder increases by an amount Δl and the diameter *decreases* by an amount Δd. If the material is perfectly elastic the strain along the X-axis ε_X is proportional to the stress,

i.e.
$$\varepsilon_X \left(= \frac{\Delta l}{l} \right) \propto \sigma_X; \quad \sigma_X = E\varepsilon_X \tag{5}$$

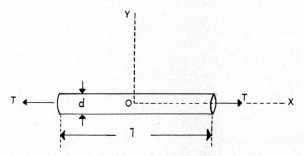

FIG. 21. Pure tensile stress.

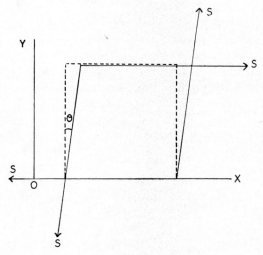

FIG. 22. Pure shear stress.

where E is called the Young's modulus of the material. Experimentally it is found that the ratio of the strain along the X-axis and the strain ε_Y, along any axis perpendicular to OX, is a constant.

$$\varepsilon_Y = \frac{\Delta d}{d}; \quad \frac{\varepsilon_Y}{\varepsilon_X} = \mu \tag{6}$$

where μ is called Poisson's ratio.

Figure 22 illustrates a second type of deformation called a shear strain. The dotted rectangle indicates an unstrained block of ice which we may suppose frozen rigidly to the ZOX plane. Suppose a force is applied tangentially to the opposite face, producing a shear stress S (the ratio of the force to the area of the face). The reactions of the support and the block of ice must produce three other shear stresses S acting in three other faces of the block as shown, if it is to remain in static equilibrium. The effect of shear stress is to distort the rectangular section to a parallelogram, rotating two faces through an angle θ. This shear strain is denoted by $\varepsilon_{XY} = \theta$, and by Hooke's Law

$$S \propto \varepsilon_{XY}; \quad S = n\theta \tag{7}$$

where n is called the modulus of rigidity or shear modulus.

The final type of strain is pure compression (or its opposite, pure dilation), such as is experienced by a *small* piece of ice immersed in a fluid. If the pressure is p and the decrease in volume V is ΔV, then

$$p = k \frac{\Delta V}{V} \tag{8}$$

and k is called the bulk modulus.

We have thus defined four elastic parameters. For an isotropic, elastic solid only two of these are independent, since it can be shown that

$$n = \frac{E}{2(1+\mu)}, \quad k = \frac{E}{3(1-2\mu)} \tag{9}$$

The rheological behaviour of a material is partly described by its stress–strain curve. That is, any one of the stresses discussed above is applied, starting from zero and increasing, and the corresponding strain is measured. The initial part of the strain–stress graph is linear. This is the elastic region where Hooke's law is obeyed. Beyond some limiting stress, called the elastic limit, the strain increases more rapidly than the stress. This is called the plastic region and is characterized by its non-linearity and by the fact that the material does not revert to its original size and shape when the stress is removed. No material is perfectly elastic for any but small strains, but this is about the only generalization possible. The range of stresses in which a material is elastic, the extent of the plastic region, and the ultimate stress at which it breaks, all vary widely between different substances. For ice we must specify the rate of stress application and this will be done more precisely later. However, if the stress is applied *rapidly* to ice, and for a short period of time only, its elastic range is quite large and the plastic range is very small, that is stresses only slightly above the elastic limit lead to fracture.

Before leaving the elastic behaviour of ice, the effect of its crystalline anisotropy should be considered. Because of its highly symmetric, hexagonal lattice it can be shown that a single crystal of ice has five independent elastic parameters, as opposed to two for an isotropic material and twenty-one for a triclinic crystalline material. Stephens (1958) reviews the measurements on the elastic properties of single crystals of ice. This work has so far found little application to polycrystalline ice and will not be discussed further.

If the crystals in a piece of ice are small and randomly oriented, its properties will be isotropic on a macroscopic scale. That is, measurements on samples large compared to the crystal size will show no anisotropy. In ice covers, the crystals are arranged with a high degree of symmetry with respect to the direction of freezing, usually, that is, with respect to the vertical. As we have seen in Chapter 2, two distinct cases arise, covering most situations, those in which the vertical direction is the direction of the c-axis of the crystals and those in which the vertical is normal to a set of randomly oriented c-axes. There is thus the possibility of four sets of elastic parameters E and μ for polycrystalline ice of an ordered type:

(1) parallel to the c-axis and the direction of freezing
(2) transverse to the c-axis and the direction of freezing
(3) parallel to the direction of freezing and transverse to a random set of c-axes
(4) transverse to the direction of freezing and in the plane of a random set of c-axes.

Presumably the ultimate strengths of polycrystalline ice may show four sets of values for the same reason. Not nearly enough experimental data are available to establish the different values of ultimate strengths and elastic parameters for the four cases, but there is evidence for slightly different values for cases (3) and (4).

Viscous Materials

If a continuous shear stress is applied to a substance, and the result is a constantly increasing shear strain, the material is called viscous. Viscous materials include all liquids and gases, and some solids, of which ice is one. A distinction is made between viscous flow and plastic flow, depending on whether a minimum shear stress must be applied to start the flow of the material. If σ and ε are the shear stress and strain, the defining equations are:

for pure viscous flow $$\frac{d\varepsilon}{dt} = f(\sigma) \tag{10}$$

for plastic flow $$\frac{d\varepsilon}{dt} = f(\sigma - \sigma_0) \tag{11}$$

where σ_0 is the limiting stress necessary for initiating flow, that is the elastic limit for shear displacements. For ice, σ_0 is small enough that it is usually ignored (although Perutz (1948) suggested that it *is* significant in glacier flow) and the response of ice to continuous stress is often considered to be purely viscous.

The form of stress function to be used in equation (10) varies considerably between materials, and for a given material $f(\sigma)$ may be a complicated function of stress, temperature and time.

The simplest case is that of Newtonian fluids which satisfy the linear equation

$$\sigma = \eta \frac{dv}{dy} \tag{12}$$

where η is the coefficient of viscosity and dv/dy is the velocity gradient transverse to the direction of flow. Referring to Fig. 22, if layers of ice parallel to ZOX have a velocity gradient dv/dy, layers at $y + dy$ and y will undergo a relative slippage of

$$[(dv/dy)\, dy\, dt \quad \text{in time} \quad dt]$$

Dividing this by dy gives the increase of strain

$$d\varepsilon = \frac{dv}{dy}\, dt$$

Hence, (12) can be written

$$\dot{\varepsilon} = \frac{d\varepsilon}{dt} = \frac{\sigma}{\eta} \tag{13}$$

Most measurements on the flow properties of ice have been made by observing the variation with time of the strain of an ice sample subjected to compressive, tensile, or flexural stress. Unless the stress is homogeneous interpretation of the results is difficult and flexural tests are of limited value for this reason. A graph of ε against time for constant σ is called a *creep curve*. The typical creep curve shows an initially large strain rate which decreases rapidly to a steady value, although at higher stresses the behaviour may be more complicated with the strain rate increasing again after its initial fall before assuming a steady value. Until recently, most experiments have been analysed by substituting the final, steady creep rate $\dot{\varepsilon}$ in equation (13) to obtain a viscosity for ice. Mantis (1951, p. 11) tabulates various values of η. One need only note that they range from $0 \cdot 002$ to 2200 (in units of 10^{12} poises) to conclude that ice is a non-Newtonian material.

A more realistic type of flow equation for ice is

$$\frac{d\varepsilon}{dt} = k\sigma^m \tag{14}$$

where m is an empirical index and k is a parameter which is temperature dependent. Glen (1958) quotes both laboratory results and glacier data giving $m \simeq 3 \cdot 1$ for stresses in the range 1 to 10 kg cm^{-2}. This equation usually fits experimental creep curves quite well, except for the initial transient creep behaviour, and for a transient effect observed when the stress is removed or reduced abruptly. When this is done, the ice shows some strain recovery (quasi-elastic behaviour) over a period of time. Glen reports that the parameter k of equation (14) decreases by a factor of about 6 in the temperature interval from -1 to $-10°C$.

Rheological studies on sea ice have been rare. Tabata (1958) measures creep curves for *in situ* beams of sea ice and for small cylinders loaded in compression. The loading time was too brief to determine which of equations (13) or (14) best described the creep. The range of temperature and salinity was small in his experiments.

Rheological Models for Ice

The combination of elastic and viscous properties possessed by ice can be represented approximately by the mechanical model shown in Fig. 23(a), consisting of a spring in series with a dashpot. This is known in rheology as a Maxwell unit. If, as is usual,

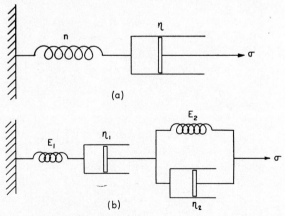

Fig. 23.   Two rheological models for ice. (a) A Maxwell unit. (b) A Maxwell unit in series with a Voigt unit.

the dashpot is taken to be a linear one in which the velocity of the piston is proportional to the applied force (corresponding to strain rate proportional to stress) the discussion above shows that it is not a very good quantitative model for ice. Nevertheless it is useful in giving a qualitative indication of the response of ice to stresses which vary with time in different manners. Let us analyse the effect on a linear system of the type of Fig. 23(a) of a sinusoidally varying shear stress, $\sigma = \sigma_0 \sin \omega t$. Let ε_E, ε_V, ε_T be the elastic, viscous, and total strains respectively. Then

$$n\varepsilon_E = \sigma \quad \text{and} \quad \eta \frac{d\varepsilon_V}{dt} = \sigma$$

$$\varepsilon_T = \varepsilon_E + \varepsilon_V$$

$$\frac{d\varepsilon_T}{dt} = \frac{d\varepsilon_E}{dt} + \frac{d\varepsilon_V}{dt} = \frac{1}{n}\frac{d\sigma}{dt} + \frac{1}{\eta}\sigma$$

$$\frac{d\varepsilon_T}{dt} = \frac{\omega\sigma_0}{n}\cos \omega t + \frac{\sigma_0}{\eta}\sin \omega t$$

Integrating, $\quad \varepsilon_T = \frac{\sigma_0}{n}\sin \omega t - \frac{\sigma_0}{\omega\eta}\cos \omega t + A$

where A is a constant of integration to be evaluated from the initial condition of zero strain, i.e. $\varepsilon_T = 0$ for $t = 0$, $A = \sigma_0/(\omega\eta)$. Hence

$$\varepsilon_T = \frac{\sigma_0}{n}\sin \omega t + \frac{\sigma_0}{\omega\eta}(1 - \cos \omega t) \tag{15}$$

Thus if $\omega \gg n/\eta$ the first term is dominant and the strain is almost entirely elastic. For pure ice a reasonable figure for n is $2\cdot5 \times 10^{10}$ dynes cm^{-2}. As we have seen above, a single value for viscosity has little meaning since the viscous flow of ice is non-linear, but a value of $\eta = 10^{10}$ poises probably gives the right order of magnitude for temperatures around $-5°C$ and stresses of about 1 kg cm^{-2}. That is, if $\omega \gg 2\cdot5$ radians per sec the strain is essentially elastic. This angular frequency corresponds to a frequency of $2 \cdot 5/2\pi = 0 \cdot 4$ cycles per sec, so that we may conclude that any periodic force with a period less than 1 sec or any steady force exerted for times of this order will result in elastic deformations of ice only. This discussion has been carried out in terms of shear stresses, but any continued stress applied to polycrystalline ice will usually result in viscous flow, so that our conclusion may be applied to any stress whether it be tensile, compressive, or flexural as well as shear.

It is possible to use a more elaborate model to analyse the visco-elastic behaviour of ice. Figure 23(b) shows the model used by Tabata (1958) in studying his creep curves in sea ice. This model puts a so-called Voigt unit in series with a Maxwell unit, and re-quires two elastic parameters and two viscosities to describe the ice. Whether this added complexity in the model is helpful in the light of the limited data available on the visco-elastic nature of ice is a moot-point.

6.2   The Ultimate Strengths of Fresh-water Ice

Because of the flow properties discussed in the last section, the stress at which an ice sample ruptures or fractures depends to some extent on the rate at which the load is applied. Jellinek (1957) measured the variation of ultimate tensile strength with rate of stress application, and found that the tensile strength observed became independent of the loading rate for rates greater than $0 \cdot 5$ kg cm^{-2} per sec. Since the tensile strength is about 15–20 kg cm^{-2} this means that a strength test should be completed to fracture in about 30 sec. Values of strengths quoted here, as well as in most of the literature, refer to values measured under this type of rapid loading.

Most strength measurements of fresh-water ice have been made on small cylinders or small bars of rectangular cross-section, with the ice at a uniform temperature. In any series of tests by one observer it is usually found that the strength increases slightly as the ice temperature decreases, and that in samples cut from an ice cover, and having a structure consisting largely of an array of vertical cylinders, the strength is greater for stresses transverse to the cylindrical axes than for those parallel to them. These differences are small, however, compared to those between different observers or even between results of one observer on ice cut from different lakes. The sample size and shape have a definite influence on the results obtained. Usually, higher strength figures are obtained for smaller test specimens and this is interpreted as meaning that ice fails at flaws in the structure. Since these flaws will be distributed statistically in the ice and will vary in their mechanical weakness, the larger the test specimen the greater the likelihood of finding a weak flaw. These reservations having been made, the figures of Table III may be taken as representative ultimate strength of fresh-water ice. They may be considered to apply to ice samples whose minimum dimension is 5 cm, and at a temperature of $-5°C$. It must be emphasized that any measurement on an individual ice sample may easily be larger or small than

TABLE III—THE ULTIMATE STRENGTHS OF FRESH-WATER ICE

Types of stress	Strength ($kg\,cm^{-2}$)	Strength (psi)
Tension	15	210
Compression (unconfined)	35	500
Shear	7	100
Flexure (bending)	17	240

the tabulated figure by a factor of two or three. The values given are not even theoretically consistent. When a beam fails in bending, one would expect that the actual rupture would occur in tension on the surface being extended, yet most observers report that ice is stronger in flexure than in pure tension.

Results of small-scale testing on ice at a uniform temperature are of limited value in applications to the bearing strength of an ice cover, which is the most important practical strength property of ice. Ice covers on rivers, lakes, and oceans are used for the crossing of men and vehicles, for aircraft landings, for storage of pulpwood, and for similar purposes. The problem involved here is rather more complex. For loads of brief duration the ice will behave elastically, but it is not at a uniform temperature and the largest stresses will develop in the warmer layers near the water. Any displacement downward of the ice will be partially offset by the buoyant force of the water. The problem of the elastic deformation of an infinite plate resting on an elastic foundation is soluble (see Wyman, 1950), and has been used as a model to calculate the bearing strength of ice. Summaries of the theory and semi-empirical tables of safe ice thicknesses are given in Mantis (1951, p. 28). Another useful reference is the proceedings of a conference on bearing strength (Legget, 1958). It must be borne in mind that an elastic theory is quite inadequate to deal with the storage of heavy loads on an ice sheet and tables of safe ice thickness for static loads are completely empirical.

The application of any theoretical equation for the bearing strength of ice requires a knowledge of its ultimate flexural strength. The most reliable values are found by in-place, beam tests in which the temperature régime of the ice cover is only very slightly disturbed. Figure 24 shows how such a test is made. The plan view of Fig. 24(a) illustrates the freely floating cantilever beam sawn out of the ice cover. The dimensions of the beam are not critical. For ice of thickness $t \leq 1$ m, a convenient shape is $l = 5t$, $b = t$ where l and b are the length and breadth of the cantilever beam. For thicker ice the length and breadth are usually made smaller in proportion to thickness to save time in preparing the test beams. A simple method of applying the load is shown in Fig. 24(b), which is a section view along the axis of the beam. A supporting beam B rests on a fulcrum on the ice sheet and on a block at the end of the cantilever. By moving a load W along B, the load on the cantilever can be increased until failure occurs. A convenient load W is an oil drum, either full of oil for small loads or containing lead weights, which can be rolled along the load supporting beam.

The test has often been varied by an arrangement in which the load is applied upwards on the end of the cantilever beam so that it fail with the lower surface in tension. These "pull-up" tests are less directly relevant to the bearing strength of ice than the "push-down" type illustrated. The flexure of a cantilever produces maximum stress in the base, or fixed end, of the beam. This stress concentration may result in stresses which are as much as twice as great as those experienced in a freely supported beam (that is, one whose support exerts no couple on it) subjected to the same load. For this reason the results obtained are undoubtedly somewhat lower than the actual flexural strength of the ice cover. Better

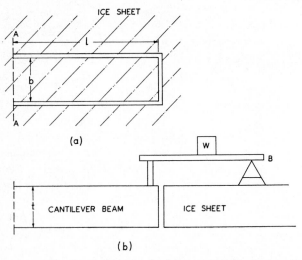

FIG. 24. In-place, cantilever beam tests for flexural strength. (a) Plan view; (b) Section view with arrangement for applying load.

results are obtained (but with a greatly increased effort) by making a further cut along the line AA in Fig. 24(a). The ends of the freely floating beam are supported by chains attached to girders lying on the ice surface transverse to the axis of the beam. These supports cannot transmit bending moment, and if the beam is now broken by applying a central load, a more reliable flexural strength is obtained. In-place beam tests are exceedingly laborious.

Frankenstein (1959) reported on a large series of cantilever beam tests on lake ice. For clear ice the flexural strength was 4·2 kg cm^{-2} (with a standard deviation of about 1·5 kg cm^{-2} on 46 tests). The corresponding figure in Table III is 17 kg cm^{-2}, showing the large difference between the results of in-place beam tests and small-scale tests. This flexural strength of 4·2 kg cm^{-2} was for tests with the surface in tension ("push-down" tests). The corresponding figure for tests with the bottom of the ice cover in tension was 5·4 kg cm^{-2}, with a standard deviation of about 1·7 kg cm^{-2} on 38 tests. At the same time Frankenstein did over 300 flexural tests on small beams (about 8 cm × 8 cm × 50 cm) cut from the same ice covers as his cantilever beams. The average flexural strength was 17·9 kg cm^{-2}, with a much larger scatter in values (from 1·5 to 39·1 kg cm^{-2}) than was found with the tests on cantilever beams. In both small-scale and large-scale tests no significant variation in strength with temperature was found, provided the ice was at −2°C or a lower temperature.

Because of the difficulty of carrying out in-place beam tests it would be a great convenience if a realistic figure on the ultimate flexural strength of an ice cover could be deduced from small-scale tests. Since the scatter on these tests is so great, single measurements are almost meaningless and a minimum of fifty samples should be measured before any confidence is placed in the average value. From Frankenstein's work it would appear reasonable, bearing in mind the stress-concentration effect in a cantilever test, to take one-half of the average flexural strength obtained on such a series as being a safe figure for the ultimate flexural strength of the ice cover.

6.3   A Theory of Sea Ice

Before discussing the strength of sea ice, it seems advisable to discuss a theoretical model of its structure which permits some predictions on how the strength will vary with the parameters of temperature and salinity. The general structure of sea ice was discussed in section 2.4. Anderson and Weeks (1958) and Assur

(1958) developed the model from this structure. Figure 25 uses Assur's notation. The ice is assumed to consist of parallel plate-lets of pure ice, with the c-axis perpendicular to the platelets. Rows of brine cylinders of elliptical cross-section are situated between the platelets. The dimensions in a plane BC, perpendicular to the growth axis G, are shown in the figure, where r_a, r_b are the

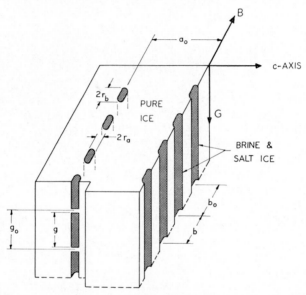

FIG. 25. A model of the structure of sea ice. The direction marked G indicates the direction of growth of the ice.

semi-axes of the ellipse, a_0 is the average platelet thickness, and b_0 the average brine cylinder separation. The brine cells are often not continuous in length, and we let g be the average length and g_0 the average separation of brine pockets along the G axis.

The weakest direction for tensile stress will be parallel to the c-axis, and for shear stress along the B axis. The tensile strength along the c-axis will be reduced because the stress is being applied to the BG plane in which the solid area is reduced by the area of the brine cylinders. It is assumed that the reduction in strength is proportional to ψ, the reduction in area. That is,

$$\sigma = \sigma_0(1 - \psi) \tag{16}$$

where σ, σ_0 are the ultimate tensile strengths with and without the brine. The stress σ_0 must include the effect of any stress concentration factor k caused by the cylindrical holes. The factor k depends on the shape of the holes. It is calculable from the theory of elasticity and has a value of about 3 to 6 for fairly rounded elliptical cross-sections to circular ones. One might think that σ_0 would equal σ_b/k where σ_b is the bulk tensile strength of pure ice, and this would probably be true if measurements could be made on "pure" ice. All actual ice, however, contains some impurities and thus presumably microscopic pockets of fluid which also act as stress concentrators. Tentatively one may therefore assume that $\sigma_b = \sigma_0$, although this assumption must be used cautiously since the imperfections in sea ice and fresh-water ice probably differ in both shape and number.

Returning to equation (16), both ψ and the brine content v can be expressed in terms of the geometry of the model. Let us introduce the dimensionless parameters $\gamma = g/g_0$ and $\beta_0 = b_0/a_0$. Then

$$\psi = \frac{2r_b}{b_0}\frac{g}{g_0} = \frac{\gamma}{\beta_0}\frac{2r_b}{a_0} \tag{17}$$

and

$$v = \frac{\pi r_a r_b}{a_0 b_0}\frac{g}{g_0} = \frac{\gamma}{\beta_0}\frac{\pi r_a r_b}{a_0^2} \tag{18}$$

From (16) and (17)

$$\sigma = \sigma_0\left(1 - \frac{\gamma}{\beta_0}\frac{2r_b}{a_0}\right) \tag{19}$$

We may reasonably assume that β_0, a_0 remain constant as v changes, so that the variation of σ with v will depend on the variation of γ and r_b with v. One plausible assumption, which seems to lead to correct results, is that γ is independent of v and that only the cross-section of the brine column changes with varying brine content, maintain the same geometrical shape. That is, that $\varepsilon = r_b/r_a$ is independent of v. On this assumption (18) becomes

$$v = \frac{\gamma}{\beta_0} \frac{\pi}{\varepsilon a_0^2} r_b^2$$

and substituting in (19)

$$\sigma = \sigma_0 \left(1 - 2\sqrt{\frac{\gamma\varepsilon}{\pi\beta_0}} \sqrt{v} \right) \tag{20}$$

These assumptions thus lead to a linear dependence of σ on $\sqrt{v}$. Two other possible assumptions may be made about the change of shape of a brine pocket with increasing temperature. One is that the brine pocket enlarges in three dimensions, maintaining a constant geometry. This leads to a linear relation between σ and $v^{2/3}$. The second is that both γ and r_a remain constant and that expansion takes place only in the dimension r_b. The section of the brine pocket thus becomes rectangular with rounded ends. This possibility arises if the ice between the brine pockets, which grew from the bridges between the initial platelets, is more readily dissolved in brine than the platelets themselves. This model leads to σ being linear with v. As we shall see later, the experimental evidence favours a $\sqrt{v}$ dependence.

One interesting consequence of (20) is that there is a limiting value of v at which σ vanishes. This no-strength condition occurs for

$$v_C = \frac{\pi\beta_0}{4\gamma\varepsilon} \tag{21}$$

and presumably gives the critical value of v at which the skeleton layer (see section 2.4) is growing.

Any experimental investigation to confirm or disprove equation (20) requires a method of calculating v from the observable paramaters of temperature, salinity, and density. Reference to Assur's table for this purpose has already been given in section 2.4. He points out that the available date on the phase diagram of sea water and ice is limited, leading to possible inaccuracies in the table, particularly at low temperatures, and that further measurements on the phase relationships in sea ice would be valuable.

6.4 Ultimate Strengths of Sea Ice

The strength parameter of sea ice most frequently measured is its ultimate tensile strength. Direct methods in which a rod is fractured by a tensile stress applied along its length are rare, and for a long time the commonest method was to find the flexural

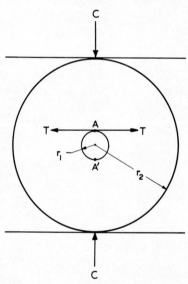

FIG. 26.   The ring tensile test on a hollow cylinder of ice.

strength of small beams by breaking them in bending. The inherent assumption that the maximum flexural stress at fracture equals the ultimate tensile strength has been discussed in section 6.2. A method which has been used extensively in recent years is the so-called ring tensile test. This test, which is illustrated in Fig. 26, was originally developed for testing concrete, and has proved very convenient for use on ice, in conjunction with a coring auger.

A core of ice, usually 3 in. (7·5 cm) in diameter, is removed from the ice and cut up into sections 3 in. long. An axial hole of 0·5 in. (1·27 cm) is drilled and the specimen is placed in a press. The compressive force C exerted by the press results in a maximum tensile stress in the hollow cylinder at the points A, A'. The force C is increased until failure occurs. The ring almost always fractures into two pieces along a diametral plane through AA'. If r_1, r_2 are the inner and outer radii of the ring the ultimate tensile strength σ_T is given by

$$\sigma_T = k \frac{C}{l\pi r_2} \tag{22}$$

where l is the length of the cylinder and k is the stress concentration factor, which is a complicated function of the ratio r_1/r_2. A graph of k is given in Assur (1958, p. 126). For $r_2/r_1 = 6$ as in the sample size cited above, $k = 7·1$. This ring tensile test is quick and lends itself to mass production methods which are so important in testing such a variable material as ice.

Extensive series of ring tensile tests on sea ice have been made by Butkovich (1956), Assur (1958), and Graystone and Langleben (1963). These last authors measured almost 400 samples at temperatures in the range -4 to $-8°C$ and found the line of best fit to be

$$\sigma_T = 29·0 - 53·3v^{\frac{1}{2}} \tag{23}$$

where σ_T is in kg cm^{-2} and v is the fractional brine content. They also analysed the data of Assur and Butkovich to obtain a similar result in the same temperature range of

$$\sigma_T = 19·7 - 46·7v^{\frac{1}{2}} \tag{24}$$

in the same units. These experiments thus agree well on a $v^{1/2}$ dependence for σ_T and on the slope of the line but differ on the extrapolated strength σ_0 for pure ice. Both values for σ_0 are significantly higher than that in Table III.

Graystone and Langleben also measured 300 samples at temperatures between −8·4°C and −20°C. Their purpose was to find if the strength increased noticeably at temperatures below −8·2°C, the critical temperature at which sodium sulphate decahydrate starts to precipitate from sea water. They concluded that the change, if any, was small and that for temperatures above −20°C, the tensile strength of sea ice depends on the brine content through a single equation of the form of (23). Assur, on the other hand, concluded that sea ice shows different intrinsic strengths in the temperature ranges of −2° to −8·2°C, −8·2° to −22·9°C, and below −22·9°C (the critical temperature for precipitation of sodium chloride dihydrate). In each range he found his data fitted equations of the type $\sigma = \sigma_0(1 - \alpha\sqrt{v})$, but with different values of σ_0 and α, so that sea ice is slightly stronger below −8·2°C and much stronger below −22·9°C for a constant value of v.

The question is of considerable practical importance. Experience in the polar regions shows qualitatively that sea ice does have different properties in the three zones of temperature. Sea ice below −23°C is greyish-white in colour (because of the precipitated salt), very hard, and somewhat brittle. If a pit is dug in a cover of sea ice whose surface temperature is below −23°C, there is a sudden colour transition at some depth to ice which has more of a green or blue shade. The temperature at the transition depth is found to be about −23°C. If a similar pit is dug in a warmer ice cover with a surface temperature of, say, −15°C, a similar transition layer at a temperature of about −8°C is found, with the ice below it being very dark and wet. It is less definite whether this dark ice is softer or weaker than the colder, greenish ice above it, but there have been reports of a noticeable decrease in the bearing strength of a thin cover of sea ice when the ice temperature rose significantly above −8°C.

Assur has attributed the increasing strength at lower temperatures to reinforcement of the mechanical strength of the ice by the solid salt deposits in it. The salt is probably deposited in the form of a hollow cylinder of mixed salt and ice, surrounding a brine cell much reduced in diameter. These numerous, tiny rods of salt and ice may reinforce the ice structure. Whether or not this is the correct explanation, it does seem definite that the strength of sea ice is considerably greater at lower temperatures ($-25°C$ and lower). There may also be a smaller increase in ice strength below $-8°C$ but this is less certain. Quantitative data, especially at very low temperatures, are unfortunately sparse.

Some in-place beam tests on sea ice have been made by Butkovich and Assur. Maximum flexural strengths of from 2 to 5 kg cm^{-2} were found for mean ice temperatures of about $-6°C$ and mean salinities of about 5‰.

Shear Strength

Pure shear stress is difficult to apply to ice, and no completely satisfactory test has been devised. Butkovich (1956) made a series of observations in which three snugly fitting cylinders each 4 in. long were slide over a 3 in. core section. Holding the end cylinders fixed, a force transverse to the axis was applied to the middle cylinder and increased until the ice failed in shear at both ends. Cores which were originally vertical in the ice cover were used so that the shear stress was applied transverse to the length of the columnar ice crystals. This partially accounts for the large values of ultimate shear stress found, although this method has been criticized on the grounds that too much support or stiffening is given to the ice sample by the cylindrical collars. Table IV summarizes the results and shows a temperature dependence for the shear stress.

TABLE IV—THE SHEAR STRENGTH OF SEA ICE

Temp. range °C	Mean temp. °C	No. of tests	Mean shear strength kg cm^{-2}	Mean S ‰	Mean v ‰
-5.5 to -7.3	-6.4	22	16.0 ± 1.1	6.3	51
-9.9 to -12.8	-11.8	21	23.8 ± 1.3	5.5	27

Compressional Strength

Unconfined compression tests have been made by many observers, usually with the stress parallel to the freezing directions. The compressional strength appears to increase with decreasing temperature and salinity, but a quantitative relation is hard to deduce because of the large scatter in results invariably found. Butkovich found values from 26 to over 107 kg cm^{-2} in the temperature range $-$ 4° to -18°C. Zubov (1945) reports values in the range 18 to 48 kg cm^{-2} for temperatures down to -30°C.

6.5 The Elastic Parameters of Ice

Many observations on the deformation of ice under static loads have been used to calculate its elastic moduli. In view of the discussion in section 6.1 it is not surprising that the results show variations of greater than an order of magnitude. Reproducible values can be found from dynamic tests, mostly by sonic and seismic means, but it is not certain if the dynamic values of E and μ are valid for static loads even if the complications of plastic flow can be avoided. Only dynamic values will be quoted.

In sonic and seismic tests, the quantities measured are usually the velocities of propagation of the various types of waves. If the sample is in the form of a rod whose length is large compared to its diameter, the compressional wave velocity c_L is given by

$$c_L = \sqrt{\frac{E}{\rho}} \tag{25}$$

where ρ is the density. When this velocity can be measured, an unambiguous value of Young's Modulus is obtained. Usually the ice is not in this form, and the velocities measured are those of the P-wave (or compressional seismic wave) c_B and the S- or shear-wave c_S. The equations for these two wave velocities are

$$c_B = c_L \sqrt{\frac{1-\mu}{(1+\mu)(1-2\mu)}} \tag{26}$$

and
$$c_S = \sqrt{\frac{n}{\rho}} = c_L \sqrt{\frac{1}{2(1+\mu)}} \qquad (27)$$

Both of these wave velocities must be measured to obtain values for E and μ. Many other types of waves can exist when solids are bounded by media, like air and water, with different elastic moduli. A number of these, such as torsional waves, Rayleigh surface waves, and air-coupled flexural waves, have been used to determine the properties of ice.

Fresh-water Ice

Perhaps the two most accurate experiments are those of Northwood (1947) and Boyle and Sproule (1931). Northwood measured c_B and c_S and checked his results by measuring the velocity of Rayleigh waves as well. He showed that for polycrystalline ice the wave velocities are essentially independent of the orientation of the ice sample and hence of mean direction of the c-axes of the crystals. No dependence of E and μ on the c-axis orientation has been established by any other observers. Northwood's values for the parameters at $-15°C$ are $E = 9·8 \times 10^{10}$ dynes cm^{-2}

$$(= 1·0 \times 10^5 \text{ kg cm}^{-2} = 1·4 \times 10^6 \text{ psi})$$

and $\mu = 0·33$.

Boyle and Sproule worked with samples to which equation (25) was applicable and found values of E ranging approximately linearly from $9·29 \times 10^{10}$ dynes cm^{-2} at $-9°C$ to $10·90 \times 10^{10}$ dynes cm^{-2} at $-35°C$. This rate of change of E with temperature must be considered as only approximate since the experiments were made outdoors and the temperatures reported are air temperatures not ice temperatures.

Sea Ice

Young's modulus for sea ice has been calculated from seismic observations on floating ice covers by a number of observers, with results ranging from $1·5 \times 10^{10}$ to $9·1 \times 10^{10}$ dynes cm^{-2}. This range reflects the very considerable changes in this parameter which occur between newly frozen ice and deteriorating spring ice on the one hand, and cold, hard winter ice on the other. Several series of tests on sea ice are reported in Langleben and Pounder (1963). These were small-scale, acoustic tests on core sections extracted from ice covers at various locations in the Arctic. The acoustic measurements were made in the field with ambient air temperatures in the range from $0°C$ to $-40°C$. Some of the tests were done on ice which resulted from freezing sea water which had been pumped up on an ice cover in winter. Because of the high freezing rate the ice was exceptionally saline, permitting observations on samples with a much higher than normal brine content. The authors found that their results fitted a linear equation

$$E = (10 \cdot 00 - 0 \cdot 0351v) \times 10^{10} \, \text{dynes cm}^{-2} \qquad (28)$$

where v is in ‰. The experimental data covered a range of values of v from almost 0 to 85‰, and were all obtained from measurements on winter ice (that is, ice less than one year old). Later experiments on polar ice did not fit equation (28) and suggested that the Young's modulus of polar ice is about 3 or 4% lower than that of winter ice.

In the same series of experiments, values of Poisson's ratio were deduced from resonance experiments with which the authors were less than completely satisfied. With some reservations, therefore, they reported that μ is relatively constant for sea ice, and apparently independent of salinity and temperature. Their average value was $\mu = 0 \cdot 295$, which is in agreement with a value of $0 \cdot 29$ reported by Peschansky (1957).

6.6   Friction

The relatively low friction between most materials and snow or ice is well known. When the frictional forces are measured carefully for different materials sliding on ice, for varying loads, and for different temperatures, the situation becomes complicated. Most of the ordinary "laws" of friction are violated. For large loading the coefficient of friction is not independent of load, but decreases fairly rapidly as the load increases, particularly at temperatures near the freezing point (Niven, 1959). At lower loads, however, Bowden (1953) has shown that Amonton's law (that the coefficient of friction is independent of the normal force) is valid. The size of the frictional force varies with temperature, the coefficient of static friction increasing by three or four orders of magnitude between $-1°$ and $-25°C$. Finally, the coefficient of kinetic friction can be much lower than the static one, and quite sensitive to speed. Bowden cites results from experiments in which various sliders were moved over ice at different speeds. For an aluminium slider on ice at $-10°C$ (to give one example), the static coefficient was 0·38, the kinetic coefficient was 0·34 at a speed of 3 cm sec^{-1} and dropped to about 0·04 at 5 m sec^{-1}.

Before discussing ice in particular, let us look at current ideas about the nature of the friction between any two solid surfaces. Many textbooks still repeat the old theory that friction results from the engagement of irregularities in the two surfaces, but if this surface roughness is thought to be on a macroscopic scale this theory is hardly tenable. Macroscopically smooth surfaces exert frictional forces at least as large as do rough ones. Try sliding one gauge block over another. It is now definitely established that friction is an adhesion process. Even when two quite smooth surfaces are pressed together, mechanical contact occurs over a very limited area only, since the surfaces will still be rough on a microscopic scale. The projections from the "average" surface are referred to as asperities. Because of the small number of asperities in contact at any time, the pressure on one of them will be many times larger than the normal force per unit surface area. It is believed that this pressure is great enough to deform plastically the asperities in contact, generating heat and, in the case of metals, even causing the asperities to weld together. Whatever the nature of the two materials, this intimate contact and working is conducive to developing strong adhesion and the frictional resistance to sliding arises from the necessity of breaking the adhesive bonds, which are thus continually formed and broken in sliding. The best modern reference on friction in general is Bowden and Tabor (1950).

Four distinct theories have been advanced to account for the low frictional resistance of snow and ice. The oldest is the pressure-melting theory, first suggested by Joly in 1886, which ascribes the low friction to lubrication by a film of water. Since ice contracts on melting, the application of pressure will lower the melting point and sufficient pressure would result in the formation of liquid water. However, when the actual area of contact between a slider and an ice surface is estimated (which can be done fairly accurately from a knowledge of the load and of the ultimate compressive strength of ice), it appears that the resulting pressure is too low for significant pressure-melting to occur except at temperatures very near to 0°C. Bowden and others have suggested that pressure-melting is negligible, but that the heat generated by the plastic deformation of the asperities on the ice surface is sufficient to melt some of the ice, that is, that the liquid film is the result of frictional heating. This frictional heating theory has found considerable acceptance, but one important piece of evidence against it should be noted. If the melting is caused by friction, the thermal conductivity of the slider should be important, and a good thermal insulator such as wood should slide more freely on ice than a material like a metal which has a high thermal conductivity (and would conduct the frictional heat away from the ice rapidly). In general this seems to be true, but magnesium, which is an excellent conductor of heat, gives very low values of friction in snow or ice.

Both of the theories discussed share the tacit assumption that a film of water, at about 0°C or slightly lower, will act as a lubricant. As Niven points out, this is a somewhat dubious assumption; very cold water, ready to freeze on the release of pressure or the loss of a small quantity of heat, is more likely to act as an adhesive than a lubricant. A good measure of the adhesive properties of the proposed water film to any material is the contact angle between the material and a drop of water. This contact angle is 0° for aluminium, ski lacquer, and nylon, that is they are completely wet by water. It is true that none of them show particularly low friction on ice, and if used as ski surfaces they are usually waxed with a hydrophobic ski wax to make them slide better. As similar evidence, teflon (polytetrafluoroethylene) is extremely hydrophobic, with a contact angle of 126°, and is probably the best ski coating known. This evidence tends to support the existence of a liquid film, but once again magnesium is exceptional because it is completely wet by water, but has such low friction on snow or ice.

As a result of extensive tests on skis of various materials, including magnesium, McConica (1950) proposed the theory of a vapour film as the lubricating agent. The water vapour would be produced by the heat of sliding friction, as in Bowden's theory. Heat transfer from a vapour to a solid is much slower than heat transfer from a liquid, so that the thermal conductivity of the slider would be of much less importance than if a liquid film were providing the lubrication. There is considerable evidence that water vapour or other gases play a role in sliding friction. The coefficient of friction for graphite is a function of the water-vapour pressure, and increases to very high values in a vacuum. Perfectly clean, out-gassed metals show much higher coefficients of friction than metal surfaces in their normal states, that is with oxide layers contained absorbed gases. It is reasonable to expect that the water-vapour pressure between a slider and ice would be a sensitive function of temperature and load, and McConica was able to account qualitatively for the great variation in the coefficient of friction on ice as these parameters vary.

The final theory is that of Niven, who attributes the low friction of solid water to the possibility of molecular rotation at the surface of an ice crystal. The possibility of this effect was noted in section 5.3, where it was pointed out that because the surface H_2O molecules do not have a complete set of hydrogen bonds to lock them into place, rotation about a single bond can take place easily. Niven suggests that the asperities of the material sliding over the ice push through this surface layer with very little expenditure of energy, the single molecules or small groups of molecules

acting somewhat like roller bearings. This disturbance of the surface layer of ice molecules is very similar to melting, and as the
asperity moves away from a particular spot on the ice, cooling
will lead to a more rigid ice-like structure, with the possibility of
adhesion to the asperity. This will clearly become more important
at lower temperatures, so that friction will increase because of
adhesion, and the specific nature of the adhesive bond between
ice and various substances will thus become more significant.

Although each of these theories has distinctive features, they do
tend to overlap somewhat, merging rather smoothly one into
another. At present it seems impossible to say clearly that one of
them is right and the others wrong. In fact, it is probable that
friction on ice involves two or even three of the processes described, with their respective contributions to the coefficient of
friction varying as the temperature and load change. Only pressure-melting seems to be ruled out, and even that may play a
part at temperatures just below the freezing point.

6.7   Density

The density of a substance is usually one of its basic properties,
but ice so often contains inclusions of foreign materials—air
bubbles, salt, etc.—that its density is variable over fairly wide
limits. As an example, consider the accumulation area of a glacier.
Snow falling intermittently builds up in thickness, the lower
layers of snow being compacted by the weight of snow above.
At some stage the compacted snow becomes ice, but where?
A vertical density profile shows a smooth increase of density with
depth and, in fact, the transition to ice is usually defined by a
change in permeability rather than one in density. The permeability of a block of snow is a measure of the ease or otherwise
with which air can move through it when a pressure difference is
established between two opposite sides. Snow is considered to
have changed to ice when the permeability drops to essentially
zero.

The density of pure ice at $0°C$ and a pressure of 1 atm is 0·9168 g cm^{-3}. Ice containing air bubbles may easily have a specific gravity under these conditions of as low as 0·86. There is no sharp lower limit to the density of bubbly ice. The specific gravity of pure ice is a function of temperature and pressure. At atmospheric pressure, the specific gravity s can be calculated from the equation

$$s = 0.9168(1 - 1.53 \times 10^{-4}\theta) \qquad (29)$$

where θ is the temperature of the ice in °C. The coefficient of volume expansion (1.53×10^{-4}) used in equation (23) was measured near 0°C, but the evidence indicates that it is practically independent of temperature. For example, at -188.7°C (liquid air) the equation gives $s = 0.9434$ and Dewar measured a value of 0·936 at this temperature, a difference of less than 1%.

If the pressure is increased above atmospheric, equation (29) must be modified to allow for the compressibility of ice. It is probably accurate enough to assume that the temperature and pressure effects are independent. Since the bulk modulus for ice is about 1.06×10^6 psi (based on Northwood's values for E and μ), the specific gravity of ice at 0°C and pressure P atmospheres is

$$s(P,0) = 0.9168[1 + 0.94 \times 10^{-7}(P-1)] \qquad (30)$$

Combining these two equations,

$$s(P,\theta) = 0.9168[1 + 0.94 \times 10^{-7}(P-1)] \cdot [(1 - 1.53 \times 10^{-4}\theta)] \qquad (31)$$

where $s(P, \theta)$ is the specific gravity at pressure P and temperature θ. The use of equation (31) is, of course, restricted to ice colder than the pressure-melting temperature. This temperature is plotted as a function of pressure in Fig. 27, using Bridgman's data. This figure shows that extremely large values of pressure are needed to lower the melting point of ice by even a few degrees, and it is for this reason that the pressure-melting hypothesis has been virtually discarded as an explanation for low friction on ice.

The density of sea ice is even more variable from sample to sample than that of fresh-water ice. Reported values range from about 0·85 to 0·94 for the specific gravity, the lowest figures referring to old surface ice from which considerable brine drainage has occurred and the highest ones to very cold winter ice. A typical figure may be taken as 0·91 for winter ice at −15°C. Curiously enough, the specific gravity of sea ice is remarkably constant with depth in a given ice cover. This results from two

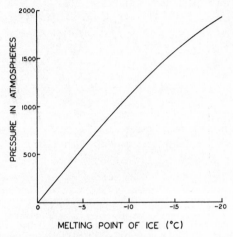

FIG. 27.   The melting point of pure ice as a function of pressure.

compensating tendencies in the freezing process. If the freezing rate increases, more salt is trapped (tending to increase density), but also more air is entrapped (tending to decrease it). For any ice cover more than a few months old, the surface layer (about the top 10% of the thickness) usually shows an increasing density with depth because of brine migration and drainage, but below this layer the density is usually constant within about $\frac{1}{2}$%.

CHAPTER 7

The Thermal and Electrical Properties of Ice

7.1 The Thermal Properties of Fresh-water Ice

Most of the experimental work on the thermal behaviour of fresh-water ice was done prior to 1938, and is reported in considerable detail in Dorsey (1940, pp. 468–82, 614–17). He gives tables of the linear and cubic coefficients of expansion of ice, of the specific and latent heats of ice, of its enthalpy, free energy, and entropy, and of its thermal conductivity and diffusivity, as functions of temperature. The discussion here will be restricted to specific and latent heats and to thermal conductivity and diffusivity.

The specific heat of ice, particularly near the freezing point, is influenced by impurities present in it. This effect is of dominating importance in the case of sea ice, which will be considered in the next section, but cannot be neglected even for ice frozen from carefully distilled water. The most accurate determinations are probably those of Dickinson and Osborne, who measured four samples of ice (of high but different purities) in the range 0° to −40°C. They found that their results were fitted by equations of the form

$$C_{obs} = a + b\theta - d/\theta^2 \tag{32}$$

where C_{obs} was the apparent specific heat (at constant pressure), θ was the temperature in °C, and a, b, d were empirical coefficients, d varying from sample to sample but a and b being the same for all samples. The value of d decreased as the purity of the sample improved, and they interpreted d/L, where L is the latent heat of fusion of ice at 0°C, as the freezing point of the solution. Their values of d/L ranged from -0.1×10^{-2} to -0.5×10^{-4}°C. On this assumption, the first two terms of equation (32) represent the true specific heat of pure ice at constant pressure, and their numerical equation was

$$C_p = \left(\frac{\partial Q}{\partial \theta}\right)_p = 0.5057 + 0.0018630\theta \tag{33}$$

where Q is the heat content of the ice, C_p is in calories per gram per °C, and the 20-degree calories is used (1 $\text{cal}_{20} = 4.183$ joules). This equation is based on measurements at atmospheric pressure, but the change in C_p with pressure is known to be small, and (33) is probably valid for pure ice under all but the most extreme pressure conditions such as at the bottom of a thick glacier.

The latent heat of fusion of pure ice at 0°C is (from Osborne) $L = 79.77 \pm 0.05 \text{ cal}_{20} \text{ g}^{-1}$. Traces of impurities in the ice have a slight influence on the value of L, but this effect can usually be neglected in fresh-water ice. The latent heat of vaporization of water at 0°C is 597 cal g^{-1}. If ice at 0°C sublimes directly to water vapour at 0°C, it is usually assumed that the total heat needed for the phase change is the sum of the above figures, namely 677 cal g^{-1}. There is some evidence that this phase change may occur in two stages, a first stage in which water evaporates with a somewhat smaller energy change because the vapour molecules still retain some degree of association, and a second stage, requiring the addition of further heat, in which the aggregates of H_2O molecules dissociate. There appear to be no experimental data on the latent heat involved when ice or snow sublimes at temperatures below 0°C. Extrapolation from known properties of water above 0°C has been made by Goff and Gratch. The Smithsonian Meteorological Tables (1951, p. 343) list the latent heat of sublimation as increasing very slowly with decreasing temperature, from 677.0 at 0°C, to 677.5 at −10°C, to 678.0 cal at −40°C. This slow change in the latent heat of sublimation results from more rapid changes in opposite directions of the latent heats of fusion and vaporization. The latent heat of fusion of water is estimated to be 79·8 at 0°C, 74·5 at −10°C, and 69·0 at −20°C. For future reference we cite the estimated specific heat of water C_w from the same tables. $C_w = 1·007$ at 0°C, 1·02 at −10°C, and 1·04 at −20°C.

The thermal conductivity k of ice is rather difficult to measure with any accuracy. The best data for pure ice are probably those of Jakob and Erk. They found $k = 5·35 \times 10^{-3}$ c.g.s. units (cal °C^{-1} cm^{-1} sec^{-1}) at 0°C. The variation in k with temperature they found to be approximately linear, and it may be represented by

$$k = 5·35 \times 10^{-3}(1 - 4·8 \times 10^{-3}\theta) \text{ c.g.s. units} \qquad (34)$$

where θ is the ice temperature in °C. The conductivity of natural ice is usually somewhat lower than equation (34) predicts because of the presence of air bubbles in the ice. These tiny air bubbles are virtually perfect insulators in comparison to ice. Schwerdtfeger (1963) has developed a theoretical equation, assuming that the air bubbles are uniformly distributed in the ice. In this case, the value of k can be calculated from the density of the ice, since ρ is a unique function of the air bubble content if there are no other impurities present. Let $k_{bi}(\theta)$ and $k_i(\theta)$ be the thermal conductivities at θ°C of the ice containing air bubbles and of pure ice respectively. Then Schwerdtfeger shows that

$$k_{bi} \approx 2k_i\left(\frac{1-v}{2+v}\right) \qquad (35)$$

where v is the fraction of the volume occupied by air. If ρ_0 is the density of pure ice and ρ that of the bubbly ice, v can be expressed in terms of ρ and ρ_0. The density of air is negligible compared to that of ice. Consider a volume of ice V, containing a volume V_i of pure ice of mass M and a volume of air V_a. Then

$$\rho_0 = \frac{M}{V_i}, \quad \rho = \frac{M}{V_i+V_a} \quad \text{and} \quad v = \frac{V_a}{V_i+V_a}$$

Eliminating V_a,
$$V_a = \frac{vV_i}{1-v}$$

and
$$\rho = \frac{M}{V_i + [vV_i/(1-v)]} = \rho_0(1-v)$$

Substituting in (35)

$$k_{bi} = \frac{2k_i\rho}{3\rho_0 - \rho} \qquad (36)$$

Equations (34) and (36) can be used to predict the thermal conductivity of pure or bubbly ice at any temperature. For example, at $-10°C$, $k_i = 5.61 \times 10^{-3}$ c.g.s. units from (34). If at this temperature the density of bubbly ice is measured as 0.8251 g cm^{-3}, then $v = 0.100$ and $k_{bi} = 4.81 \times 10^{-3}$ c.g.s. units, taking $\rho_0 = 0.9168$ g cm^{-3} and neglecting changes in density with temperature.

The diffusion equation, to be discussed in Chapter 8, is the basic differential equation giving the temperature distribution in a solid in terms of the boundary conditions. The properties of the solid appear in this equation in terms of a single parameter K, called the diffusivity, and defined as

$$K = \frac{k}{\rho C_p} \qquad (37)$$

where k, ρ, and C_p are the thermal conductivity, density, and specific heat of the material. The diffusivity can be calculated from (37) and for pure ice at $0°C$, $K = 1.15 \times 10^{-2}$ cm^2 sec^{-1}. The factor k on the right-hand side of the equation is the one known with least accuracy.

Experimen tally, equation (37) has often been used to determine k. In fact, most of the values in the literature of the thermal conductivity of ice were obtained from a study of the temperature di stribution in an ice cover, so that K was the quantity actually m easured and k was deduced from it.

7.2   The Thermal Properties of Sea Ice

Since sea ice in its natural state always contains cells or pockets of liquid brine, any change of temperature of the ice will involve a phase change of some of the water substance, from water to ice for a temperature decrease and vice versa for an increase. For this reason the concepts of specific and latent heats are strongly interrelated, and in fact the idea of a definite latent heat of fusion must be abandoned since the phase change from solid to liquid is a continuous process. At any temperature, the quantity of heat required to give unit mass of sea ice a small increment of temperature is always greater than that needed to raise the temperature of unit mass of pure ice to the same extent. The difference is small for ice of low salinity at temperatures below $-10°C$, but the specific heat of sea ice rises very rapidly as the melting point is approached, particularly if the salinity is high. Because the thermal properties of sea ice are largely controlled by its salinity, and because the salt content of ice depends markedly on the freezing rate, the phase change from sea ice to sea water is not thermodynamically reversible; it is most unlikely that a sample of sea ice melted and then cooled to its original temperature will regain the same salinity and thermal properties it had originally.

Comparatively little experimental work has been done on the thermal behaviour of sea ice, and the classic work of Malmgren (1927) has been the standard reference for years. A recent paper by Schwerdtfeger (1963) is a useful contribution to this field. He has analysed sea ice as a mixture of pure ice, air, water, and dissolved and precipitated salts and has derived theoretical equations for the specific heat and latent heat of freezing, for the density, and for the thermal conductivity and diffusivity, as functions of salinity and temperature. In the last two cases, the model of section 6.3 was assumed. Numerous tables and graphs of these parameters are given. Although this was primarily a theoretical study, Schwerdtfeger did make some laboratory measurements on the specific heat of sea ice, obtaining good agreement between theory and experiment, and also attempted to evaluate the thermal conductivity from a field study on sea ice in Hudson Bay. The value of k obtained from this work was not of very high accuracy and can hardly be considered as an adequate verification of his theoretical work on thermal conductivity. An outline of the approach is given below, and the paper should be consulted for further details.

The starting point is Fig. 28, a phase diagram for sea ice, taken from Assur (1958) and based on the work of Nelson and Thompson. In this diagram the freezing point θ of brine (of the same composition as normal sea water) is plotted as a function of s, the ratio by weight of dissolved salts to pure water. Note that θ is plotted against s and not against the salinity σ (the notation of Schwerdtfeger's paper is used here for convenience of reference). The advantage of using s as the parameter is that for ideal solutions $s \propto \theta$, whereas θ is not a linear function of σ. The graph shows that this linear relation is indeed observed down to a temperature of about $-8°C$, where $Na_2SO_4.10H_2O$ starts to precipitate. Below this temperature the graph is again linear, but with a different slope, down to about $-23°C$, where $NaCl.2H_2O$ starts to precipitate. The equations of the two linear portions of the freezing graph are:

$$s = -1·848\theta \times 10^{-2}, \quad 0 \geqq \theta \geqq -7·6°C$$

$$s = (6·240 - 1·031\theta) \times 10^{-2}, \quad -7·6°C \geqq \theta \geqq -23°C$$

If we write p for the fractional weight of the precipitated salt (*not* including its water of crystallization), these equations can be written

$$s = \alpha\theta, \quad 0 \geqq \theta \geqq -7·6 \tag{38}$$

$$s + p = \alpha\theta, \quad p = \alpha'(\theta + 7·6), \quad -7·6 \geqq \theta \geqq -23 \tag{39}$$

where $\alpha = -1·848 \times 10^{-2}$, $\alpha' = -1·031 \times 10^{-2}$ per °C.

Consider first the case of ice at a temperature above $-8°C$. All the salt in the ice will be in solution in the brine cells. If the

5   POI

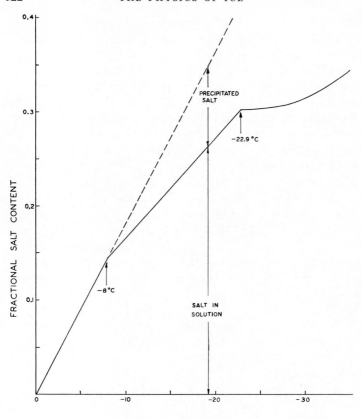

FIG. 28.   The freezing point of brine as a function of its salt content.

salinity of the ice as a whole is σ and the fractional salt content of the brine is s, unit mass of sea ice (1 g) contains σ grams of salts and $(1 - \sigma)$ g of H_2O. Most of the H_2O is solid, pure ice but there must be a mass w of liquid water forming a brine with the salt. Then

$$s = \frac{\sigma}{w}, \quad w = \frac{\sigma}{s}$$

and the mass of pure ice is

$$m = 1 - \sigma - w = 1 - \sigma - \frac{\sigma}{s} \qquad (40)$$

A temperature change will alter both s and w and

$$dw = -\frac{\sigma}{s^2}\,ds = -\frac{\sigma\alpha\,d\theta}{\alpha^2\theta^2}$$

from (38). We now assume that the contributions to the change in the heat content of the sea ice resulting from the specific heat of the salt itself and from its heat of crystallization or dilution are both negligible. The change in heat content with temperature thus contains three significant terms, arising from the latent heat associated with the phase change of dw, the specific heat of the pure ice, and the specific heat of the pure water. Hence

$$dQ = L_i\,dw + mC_i\,d\theta + wC_w\,d\theta$$

$$dQ = -L_i\frac{\sigma\,d\theta}{\alpha\theta^2} + \left(1 - \sigma - \frac{\sigma}{\alpha\theta}\right)C_i\,d\theta + \frac{\sigma}{\alpha\theta}C_w\,d\theta$$

where L_i is the latent heat of pure ice and C_i, C_w are the specific heats of pure ice and water. Then if C_s is the specific heat of sea ice

$$C_s = \frac{dQ}{d\theta} = \frac{-\sigma}{\alpha\theta^2}L_i + \frac{\sigma}{\alpha\theta}(C_w - C_i) + C_i(1 - \sigma) \qquad (41)$$

In calculations with this equation σ must be expressed as a fraction.

Next we show that this equation is essentially correct for the temperature range $-8°$ to $-23°C$ also. In this range some of the salt has precipitated as $Na_2SO_4.10H_2O$. Unit mass of sea ice now contains w grams of water, ws grams of dissolved salt, wp grams of precipitated salt, and βwp grams of water of crystallization combined with the precipitated salt. From the chemical formula of the hydrated sodium sulphate, $\beta \cdot 27$. The composition of unit mass of sea ice is thus:

$$1 = (\sigma - wp)(\text{salt in the brine}) + (1 - \sigma - w - \beta wp)(\text{pure ice})$$
$$+ w(\text{water in the brine}) + \beta wp(\text{water of crystallization})$$
$$+ wp(\text{precipitated salt})$$

The mass of salt $\sigma = ws$ (salt in solution) $+ wp$ (precipitated salt). That is,

$$w = \frac{\sigma}{s+p}, \quad dw = -\sigma \frac{ds+dp}{(s+p)^2} \quad (42)$$

Hence, the heat dQ absorbed by unit mass of sea ice when its temperature rises by $d\theta$ is

$$dQ = L_i dw + (1 - \sigma - w - \beta wp)C_i d\theta + wC_w d\theta + (wp + \beta wp)C_h d\theta \quad (43)$$

where C_h is the specific heat of the hydrated sodium sulphate. Substituting from (42) and (39)

$$dQ = -L_i \sigma \frac{(ds+dp)}{(s+p)^2} + \left[1 - \sigma - \frac{\sigma(1+\beta p)}{s+p}\right]C_i d\theta + \frac{\sigma}{s+p}C_w d\theta$$
$$+ \left[\frac{\sigma p}{s+p}(1+\beta)\right]C_h d\theta$$

$$dQ = -L_i \frac{\sigma d\theta}{\alpha\theta^2} + \left[1 - \sigma - \frac{\sigma}{\alpha\theta}(1+\beta p)\right]C_i d\theta + \frac{\sigma}{\alpha\theta}C_w d\theta$$
$$+ \frac{\sigma p}{\alpha\theta}(1+\beta)C_h d\theta \quad (44)$$

In equation (44), the contribution to dQ from the specific heat of the salt in the brine is neglected, but the contribution from the specific heat of the hydrated salt is included because it may be significant owing to the water of crystallization. The specific heat C_s is thus:

$$C_s = \frac{-L_i \sigma}{\alpha\theta^2} + \frac{\sigma}{\alpha\theta}(C_w - C_i) + C_i(1-\sigma) + \frac{\sigma p}{\alpha\theta}[(1+\beta)C_h - \beta C_i] \quad (45)$$

The last term in (45) can be written with the aid of (39) as

$$\sigma \frac{\alpha'}{\alpha} \frac{\theta + 7\cdot6}{\theta} [(1+\beta)C_h - \beta C_i]$$

In this expression $\sigma \lesssim 10^{-3}$, $\alpha'/\alpha < 1$, $(\theta + 7\cdot6)/\theta < 1$ and each of the terms in the square bracket is of the order of 1. Hence the expression $\gtrsim 10^{-3}$ and can be neglected in comparison with the other terms in (45), which thus reduces to the same equation as (41).

At temperatures below $-23°C$, the relation between s and θ is no longer linear and the analysis is more difficult but less important because (as can be seen from Table V) the specific heat is tending towards a constant value, of about $0\cdot5$ cal g^{-1} °C^{-1}, which is only slightly influenced by the salinity of the ice.

Table V gives the values of C_s between $-2°$ and $-22°C$, calculated from equation (41) using the values of the parameters given in section 7.1. The numerical values differ slightly from those of Schwerdtfeger and are believed to be more accurate.

Latent Heat and Heat of Melting

As discussed above, there is no true latent heat of melting for sea ice since the phase change is continuous from sea ice to sea water. The latent heat of ice formation is still a useful concept however. It can be calculated as follows. Sea water of a definite salinity S freezes at a particular temperature, and if the sea water is cooled to this temperature a certain amount of pure ice will form and some brine will be trapped in it. Using σ and s as above to stand for the salinity of the sea ice as a whole and the fractional salt content of the brine, the mass of pure ice in unit mass of sea ice is $m = 1 - \sigma - (\sigma/s)$ and the quantity of heat released in freezing it is

$$L_s = \left(1 - \sigma - \frac{\sigma}{s}\right) L_i \tag{46}$$

TABLE V—THE SPECIFIC HEAT OF SEA ICE IN CAL G^{-1} C DEG^{-1}

Salinity of ice $^o/_{oo}$	Temperature in °C										
	-2	-4	-6	-8	-10	-12	-14	-16	-18	-20	-22
0	0·50	0·50	0·49	0·49	0·49	0·48	0·48	0·48	0·47	0·47	0·46
1	1·58	0·77	0·61	0·56	0·53	0·51	0·50	0·50	0·48	0·48	0·47
2	2·66	1·04	0·73	0·62	0·58	0·54	0·52	0·51	0·50	0·49	0·48
4	4·81	1·58	0·97	0·76	0·66	0·60	0·56	0·55	0·52	0·51	0·50
6	6·97	2·12	1·21	0·89	0·75	0·66	0·61	0·58	0·55	0·53	0·51
8	9·13	2·65	1·45	1·03	0·83	0·72	0·65	0·61	0·57	0·55	0·53
10	11·3	3·19	1·68	1·16	0·92	0·78	0·69	0·65	0·60	0·57	0·55

The value of s is not known. One assumption is that the salinity of the trapped brine equals that of the sea water from which the ice is growing, that is, that

$$s = \frac{S}{1-S} \qquad (47)$$

This assumption cannot be exactly correct because, as the platelets of pure ice grow, there is continual rejection of salt into the brine between the platelets. There is thus a concentration gradient from the brine to the sea water below the ice so that when some of the brine is cut off from the melt its salt content must be slightly higher than given by (47). This process also occurs in the freezing of metals, and the existence of abnormally high concentrations of impurities in the melt is described by the terms constitutional supercooling. The phenomenon is believed to be of great importance in determining the type of crystal growth which occurs. The excess of s over the value given by (47) is not known in sea ice, but it is probably small, and combining (46) and (47) is unlikely to lead to serious error. Thus

$$L_s \approx \left[1 - \sigma - \frac{\sigma(1-S)}{S} \right] L_i$$

$$L_s \approx \left(1 - \frac{\sigma}{S} \right) L_i \qquad (48)$$

This equation was first given by Malmgren.

Because the salinity of sea ice is much lower than that of sea water, sea ice removed from contact with the sea water melts at a higher temperature than the freezing point of the sea water. The quantity of heat required to melt completely an isolated specimen of sea ice at a given initial temperature can be found by integrating equation (41), and Schwerdtfeger gives a table of values of this heat of melting. The results are not valid for the melting of an ice cover *in situ*, because at a fairly early stage in the decay of an ice cover it becomes permeable to sea water and thereafter melts with its brine cells in contact with sea water. The complexity of this situation was discussed in section 2.4.

Thermal Conductivity

Both Anderson (1960) and Schwerdtfeger (1963) have derived theoretical equations for the thermal conductivity of sea ice using the model of section 6.3, and other models as well. Schwerdtfeger includes the effect of air bubbles in the ice. The most important models are those in which the pure (or bubbly) ice is considered to consist of parallel plates separated by films of brine or rows of brine cells. Since the thermal conductivity of the brine is lower than that of the pure ice, the k value for sea ice will always be smaller than for pure ice. If the heat flow is parallel to the brine cells, the ice and brine can be considered as parallel conductors and since most of the heat will flow through the pure ice the reduction in k will be roughly proportional to the fraction of the cross-sectional area occupied by brine, that is, $k_s \sim k_i(1-v)$, where k_s and k_i are the conductivities of sea ice and pure ice. If the heat flow is parallel to the c-axis the ice and brine are exactly in series in the plate and brine-film model and approximately so if the brine is in rows of cylinders. Hence the thermal conductivity of sea ice should be significantly less parallel to the c-axis than transverse to it.

Both authors calculate that the thermal conductivity of sea ice can vary by at least a factor of two with changes in salinity and temperature, and should approach the value for fresh-water ice asymptotically at temperatures below about $-15°$ or $-20°C$.

Schwerdtfeger points out that the diffusivity K (equation (37)) of sea ice is especially sensitive to temperature change, because an increase in temperature will decrease k and increase both ρ and C_s. All three factors thus cause K to decrease rapidly with increasing temperature.

7.3 The Electrical Properties of Fresh-water Ice

In a perfect single crystal of pure ice at temperatures well below the freezing point, it is believed that the number of free electrons is negligible, so that if a d.c. field is applied the only mechanism available for electrical conduction is the "proton-jump" process described in section 5.4. Any actual sample of ice will contain impurities which will probably have a major effect on the electrical conductivity. Polarization effects at the surfaces of the sample and at internal surfaces such as cracks, gas bubbles and inter-crystalline boundaries will also mask the true conductivity of ice. As a result the d.c. measurements of conductivity which have been made show extremely wide scatter, and one can only say that the conductivity σ of pure ice is extremely low, $\sigma \sim 10^{-8}$ to 10^{-9} (ohm-cm)$^{-1}$ being a reasonable guess. If this is the right order for σ, pure ice falls in the semiconductor class, and attempts have been made to describe conduction in pure ice in terms of both proton and hole (lattice defect) movements.

When an alternating field is applied to ice, additional phenomena appear. Ice has no permanent electric dipole moment but is readily polarized, presumably both by shifts in the electron cloud distribution and by proton jumps. When the induced dipole moment is reversed as the field reverses, some of the electrical energy is dissipated as heat in the lattice. This dissipative effect, called dielectric absorption, gives rise to an effective electrical conductivity σ_e which is much larger than the true electrical conductivity in the previous paragraph.

The dielectric behaviour of ice is usually discussed in terms of the Debye theory (see Debye, 1929). If C_0 is the capacitance of a capacitor in a vacuum and C is its capacitance when immersed in a medium, then $\varepsilon = C/C_0$ is called the dielectric coefficient (or often, in a poor terminology, the dielectric constant) of the medium. If the material shows dielectric absorption, the effective dielectric coefficient can be written as a complex quantity

$$\varepsilon = \varepsilon' - i\varepsilon'' \qquad (49)$$

where ε' is the true dielectric coefficient and ε'' is associated with the energy losses. The capacitor will have a phase angle of $90 - \phi$ where ϕ is called the phase defect and $\tan \phi$ the loss tangent. Then

$$\tan \phi = \varepsilon''/\varepsilon' \tag{50}$$

$$\sigma_e = \omega k_0 \varepsilon'' \tag{51}$$

where ω is the angular frequency of the alternating field,

$$k_0 = 8{\cdot}85 \times 10^{-12} \text{ farad } m^{-1}$$

is the permittivity of free space, and equation (51) is in m.k.s. units. Equations (50) and (51) can be derived easily by considering the equivalence between a capacitor with the lossy dielectric of (49) and a parallel combination of pure resistance and pure capacitance.

Since distortion of the charge distribution of the H_2O molecule in ice requires some time, the value of ε will depend on the frequency of the alternating field, with two limiting values: $\varepsilon \to \varepsilon_0$, a constant value, as ω becomes large (optical frequencies) and $\varepsilon \to \varepsilon_1$ at $\omega = 0$ (the d.c. case). The reason for the constancy of ε_0 is presumably that at optical frequencies the field reverses too fast for proton jumps to occur in significant numbers and the dielectric behaviour arises only from polarization of the electron clouds. The time for the induced dipole moment to "decay" is introduced into the theory in terms of a relaxation time τ, where τ is the time for the polarization of the ice to reduce to $1/e$

$$(e = 2{\cdot}718)$$

of its initial value when the (constant) electric field producing it is turned off.

Introducing the parameter $\alpha = 2\pi\tau(\varepsilon_1 + 2)/(\varepsilon_0 + 2)$, the assumptions of the Debye theory lead to the so-called Drude–Debye relations:

$$\varepsilon' = \frac{\varepsilon_1 + \varepsilon_0 \alpha^2 f^2}{1 + \alpha^2 f^2} \tag{52}$$

$$\varepsilon'' = \frac{(\varepsilon_1 - \varepsilon_0)\alpha f}{1 + \alpha^2 f^2} \tag{53}$$

where f is the frequency $(= \omega/2\pi)$ in cycles per second. The parameter α is independent of frequency but has an empirically determined temperature dependence given by

$$\alpha = \alpha_0 \, e^{-\beta\theta} \qquad (54)$$

The best numerical values appear to be $\varepsilon_1 = 74\cdot6$, $\varepsilon_0 = 3\cdot0$, $\alpha_0 = 1\cdot16 \times 10^{-4}$ sec, and $\beta = 0\cdot101$ $(°C)^{-1}$. Equations (52) and (53) agree fairly well with experimental measurements in the temperature range $0°$ to $-70°C$ and the frequency range d.c. to 10^{10} c/s. Equation (50), and presumably therefore equation (53), fails completely at frequencies higher than 10^{10} c/s, and it must be assumed that a change occurs at high frequencies in the method of energy dissipation. Another discrepancy is that the index of refraction n should equal $\sqrt{\varepsilon'}$. At optical frequencies $\varepsilon' = \varepsilon_0$ and $\sqrt{\varepsilon_0} = 1\cdot73$, which is considerably higher than the observed refractive index for ice of $n = 1\cdot31$.

It should be emphasized that the numerical values of the various parameters quoted above were deduced from measurements on ice frozen from water of high purity. Particularly at the lower frequencies, impurities may have a large effect on the dielectric coefficient as well as the conductivity of ice. Mantis (1951) and Dorsey (1940) may be consulted for details of the experimental observations and literature references. More recent work may be found from a paper of Jaccard (1959).

7.4 The Electrical Properties of Sea Ice

Since sea ice has the array of cylindrical brine cells which has been referred to so often, its electrical behaviour will be dominated by these low resistance filaments. Anisotropy of electrical conductivity and dielectric coefficient with respect to the direction of the c-axis may be expected to be large. Anderson (1960) has developed theoretical expressions for the electrical conductivity using the same approach used for thermal conductivity. Very few experimental observations exist. Dichtel and Lundquist (1951) made four-terminal d.c. measurements on natural sea ice covers and found resistivities in the horizontal direction of about 10^2 to 10^4 ohm-metres and in the vertical direction of about 10^2 ohm-metres. Cook (1960) made capacitance measurements at 100 Mc/s on artificial sea ice, transverse to the freezing direction. He found dielectric coefficients of about 3 or 4, similar to the value for pure ice at this frequency, and resistivities comparable to those of Dichtel and Lundquist.

J. R. Addison (unpublished results of experiments at McGill University) has measured the capacitive and resistive components parallel to the freezing direction of artificially frozen sea ice. All observations were on ice at $-22°C$ and the frequency range covered was from 20 c/s to 50 Mc/s. He found apparent, very high dielectric coefficients of the order of 10^5 to 10^6 at the lowest frequency. The value of ε' decreased approximately as $1/\omega$ in the audio range (up to about 100 kc/s) and more slowly in the r.f. range, reaching values of about 10 at 50 Mc/s. The effective resistivity ρ_e also decreased with frequency, but much more slowly than the dielectric coefficient. Values of ρ_e were about 500 at 1 kc/s, 120 at 1 Mc/s, and 60 at 50 Mc/s, all in ohm-metres. The salinity of all the ice samples was high, about 10‰. The extraordinarily large values of ε' at low audio frequencies are probably a result of ionic mobility in the brine cells. Some charge separation must occur when an electric field is applied and since the brine cells may be several centimetres long, they act as macroscopic dipoles. The variation with frequency as $1/\omega$ is evidence that the ionic mobility is independent of frequency and field strength, although it probably varies with temperature.

CHAPTER 8

The Growth and Decay of an Ice Cover

FOR purposes of navigation and similar practical matters, it is important to be able to predict the date at which an ice cover starts to form on a body of water, the rate at which it will thicken, and the maximum thickness which will be obtained. Equally important are the converse problems of decay—when will the ice become unsafe for travel, and when will the ice cover break up? As with other geophysical forecasting such as weather predictions, completely correct forecasts will probably never be attained, but considerable success has been achieved with the problems of ice growth. The factors influencing the decay of ice are less well understood.

8.1 Stefan's Law and the Diffusion Equation

The first mathematical description of ice growth was made by Stefan in 1891, along the following lines. Let the temperature difference between the top surface of an ice cover and the water under it be θ at a time t when the ice thickness is h. Then the mean temperature gradient is θ/h and the quantity of heat conducted upward through the ice per unit area in time $\mathrm{d}t$ is $\mathrm{d}Q = k(\theta/h)\,\mathrm{d}t$ —where k is the mean thermal conductivity. The source of this heat is the latent heat released by freezing an additional thickness $\mathrm{d}h$ of ice. This must be, per unit area, $L\rho\,\mathrm{d}h$ where L is the latent heat and ρ the density of the ice. Hence

$$k\frac{\theta}{h}\mathrm{d}t = L\rho\,\mathrm{d}h$$

which integrates to $\quad h^2 = \dfrac{2k}{L\rho} \displaystyle\int_{t_0}^{t} \theta \, \mathrm{d}t = \dfrac{2k}{L\rho} E_t$ (55)

In this equation t_0 is the time when ice first started to form, and the integral E_t is called the freezing exposure. The freezing exposure is usually quoted in degree-days or degree-months, and the temperature θ should be the depression of the temperature of the top *ice* surface below 0°C in the case of fresh-water ice, or below the freezing point of the sea water ($-1\cdot9$°C for normal salinity). The actual ice temperature is only rarely available, and E_t is often calculated in retrospect from meteorological records of air temperature, or forecast from similar climatological data. Such calculations must be used with caution since the air temperature is measured by meteorologists at a point about 4 ft above the surface and may not be a good measure of the surface temperature. Even more serious is the effect of a snow cover on the ice. Snow is usually an excellent heat insulator and a considerable temperature difference often exists between the ice–snow interface and the air.

The derivation of equation (55) neglects the specific heat of the ice; that is, the latent heat is only the heat removed on the initial formation of the ice, and as the cover grows in thickness it cools to much lower temperatures (especially the upper layers) releasing additional heat to the atmosphere. Despite these limitations, Stefan's law, that ice thickness varies as the square root of the freezing exposure, is found to describe ice growth under a remarkably wide variety of conditions, and it is still the principal tool in forecasting ice growth, although empirical coefficients are usually substituted for the theoretical value in (55). The empirical coefficient is chosen from past experience with the type of ice and snow cover expected. Assur (1956) gives coefficients for various conditions.

Many attempts have been made to develop more general solutions to the problem of ice growth, taking into account the effects of the snow cover, the specific heat of the ice, the non-linear temperature gradient in the ice, and so on. Kolesnikov (1958) discusses various solutions with references. Although more satisfying theoretically, these solutions are usually too involved and require too much unavailable data to be of much practical use.

The Diffusion Equation

The temperature distribution in a solid is governed by the solution of a differential equation called the diffusion equation, with appropriate boundary conditions. This equation can be derived

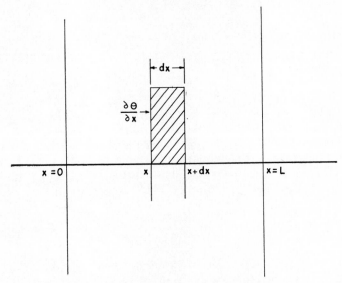

FIG. 29.   The temperature gradient in an infinite slab.

as follows, taking one-dimensional heat flow for convenience. Figure 29 represents an infinite slab of material whose thermal conductivity, density, and specific heat are respectively k, ρ, and C. Each of these parameters may be a function of x. The slab is bounded by isothermal faces at $x = 0$ and $x = L$. Heat flow under these conditions will take place parallel to the x-axis only. Let $\theta(x, t)$ be the temperature at any point in the slab at time t.

Consider the quantity of heat in unit area of the section of the material between x and $x+dx$. The temperature gradient normal to the face at x is $\partial\theta/\partial x$. The heat flow per unit area is $-k$ times the temperature gradient, the negative sign indicating that the heat flows in the opposite direction to the temperature gradient. Thus the gain of heat per unit time through unit area at x is $-k(\partial\theta/\partial x)$. Similarly the loss of heat per unit time through unit area at $x+dx$ is

$$\left(-k\frac{\partial\theta}{\partial x}\right)+\frac{\partial}{\partial x}\left(-k\frac{\partial\theta}{\partial x}\right)dx$$

where any variation of k with x is allowed for in this expression. Thus the net gain of heat per unit time in the shaded volume of Fig. 29 is

$$\left(-k\frac{\partial\theta}{\partial x}\right)-\left[\left(-k\frac{\partial\theta}{\partial x}\right)+\frac{\partial}{\partial x}\left(-k\frac{\partial\theta}{\partial x}\right)dx\right]=\frac{\partial}{\partial x}\left(k\frac{\partial\theta}{\partial x}\right)dx$$

This gain of heat will raise the temperature of this volume of the material, and the gain of heat per unit time can also be expressed as $\partial(C\theta\rho\,dx)/\partial t$. Equating these two expressions gives the most general one-dimensional form of the diffusion equation as

$$\frac{\partial}{\partial x}\left(k\frac{\partial\theta}{\partial x}\right)=\frac{\partial}{\partial t}(C\rho\theta) \tag{56}$$

Mathematical solutions of this equation are very difficult to find unless k, C, and ρ are constants. In this case (56) becomes

$$\frac{\partial\theta}{\partial t}=\frac{k}{C\rho}\frac{\partial^2\theta}{\partial x^2}=K\frac{\partial^2\theta}{\partial x^2} \tag{57}$$

where K is the diffusivity.

The flow of heat in an ice cover is usually one-dimensional, but if more involved situations are encountered in which

$$\theta=\theta(x,y,z,t),$$

equation (57) can easily be generalized to

$$\frac{\partial \theta}{\partial t} = K \left[\frac{\partial^2 \theta}{\partial x^2} + \frac{\partial^2 \theta}{\partial y^2} + \frac{\partial^2 \theta}{\partial z^2} \right] \tag{58}$$

A large part of theoretical physics is concerned with the solution of partial differential equations such as (58), under known boundary and initial equations. Pounder (1960) gives solutions of two simple cases of heat flow in ice, one of which will be summarized here because it points out the important physical fact that heat flow takes time, and a change in the air temperature at the surface of ice will not cause a change in the ice temperature at an internal point until after some considerable time has elapsed. Figure 30 shows an idealized situation in which a step change occurs in the air temperature above an ice cover. The water temperature is fixed at $0°$ (on some suitable temperature scale) and the air temperature remains at θ_0 for a long time. This situation gives a linear temperature gradient in the ice, as shown. At zero time, let the air temperature drop abruptly to θ_1 and remain fixed thereafter. The problem is to find $\theta(x, t)$ at future times. Eventually the temperature in the ice will reach the linear relation shown by the dotted line, but what sort of times are involved? If it is assumed that the top surface of the ice immediately takes on the new temperature θ_1 (and the fallacy in this assumption will be discussed below), that K is a constant, and that the growth in ice thickness can be neglected, the solution of (57) under these conditions is a simple application of Fourier analysis, leading to the relation

$$\theta(x, t) = \theta_1 \frac{x}{h} + \sum_{n=1}^{\infty} (-1)^{n+1} \frac{2(\theta_0 - \theta_1)}{n\pi} \exp \frac{(-n^2 \pi^2 K t)}{h^2} \sin \frac{(n\pi x)}{h}$$

$$\tag{59}$$

Since time appears in this equation only in the factor t/h^2 one can see that the time for a temperature disturbance at the surface to reach a certain fractional depth in the ice cover increases as the square of the total thickness.

To go further, some number must be substituted. In Pounder's paper the ice thickness h was taken as 50 cm and K as 3.34×10^{-3} c.g.s. units. The temperature was calculated at $x = h/4$, that is at three-quarters of the way down through the ice cover. Figure 31

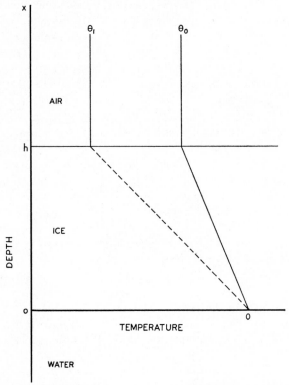

FIG. 30.   A model for evaluating the effect on an ice cover of an abrupt change in the air temperature.

shows the result, and indicates that about 75 % of the effect of the surface temperature change should have penetrated to this level in about two days. The effect of this reduced temperature would be an increase in the freezing rate, and in the actual case, which the mathematical model was simulating, an increased freezing rate *was* observed—but some eight to ten days after the drop in air temperature. The discrepancy undoubtedly arises from the assumption that the ice at $x = h$ has the same temperature as the air. Even if the ice is in contact directly with the air (no snow cover), it is a well-known experimental result in heat conduction that a thin stationary layer of air adjoins the solid surface. There

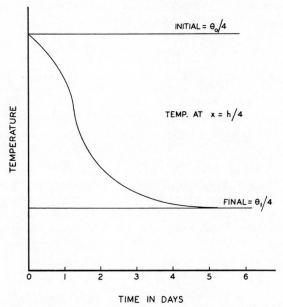

FIG. 31. The theoretical temperature variation with time at a fixed depth in an ice cover after the air temperature change of Fig. 30.

is a significant temperature gradient across the boundary layer, so that the ice is warmer than the air a few centimetres above it. The thickness of this layer (and hence its insulating effectiveness) is not constant but varies with wind speed.

The above results are rather typical of the theory of heat conduction. The theory is very helpful in understanding the phenomena but can usually only give orders of magnitude for the numerical results which are found experimentally, because models which can be solved mathematically are over-simplified versions of the complex physical situation. Conditions in a cover of sea ice are particularly difficult to analyse mathematically because the diffusivity K (and the three parameters which make it up) varies not only with depth (because of temperature changes with depth) but also with time (because of temperature and salinity changes with time). Schwerdtfeger (1964) has described an analogue computer which should be useful in solving the diffusion equation in sea ice.

8.2 The Heat Budget Before and After Freeze-Up

The preceding section has outlined some of the theoretical methods of dealing with ice growth after ice has started to form. The problem of predicting the date of freeze-up is of a rather different type. As soon as the air temperature falls below the surface temperature of the water, heat is lost from the surface by a number of mechanisms, principally convective cooling by the air, evaporation, and radiation. Some of these factors (particularly radiation) may at times give rise to a temporary heat gain by water during the cooling period. Loss of heat from the surface of the water sets up convective circulation, as discussed in section 1.3, and the upper portions of the water cool until the freezing point is reached. Many countries maintain records of the dates of freeze-up of major lakes and rivers. Particularly in the case of lakes, there is relatively little variation in the date of freeze-up from year to year, and this synoptic approach to forecasting has proved to be the most satisfactory for fresh-water ice.

More variation exists in the time of freeze-up of sea water because the relevant oceanographic parameters are apparently more changeable than the corresponding limnological ones. Predictions are usually based on the "ice potential" method introduced by Zubov in 1938. Data from oceanographic stations give information on the depth of the thermocline (halocline) and the salinity and temperature distribution above it. Theoretical models for the rate of convective mixing and the rate of heat transfer to the air must be assumed. Based on these and climatological data on the expected air temperatures, an estimate can be made of the date at which the surface water will reach the freezing point (Simpson, 1958).

Once a cover of sea ice has formed, the only property of the sea water of importance is its salinity, which establishes the temperature of the lower face of the ice cover. The sea can then be treated as an infinite reservoir of heat whose release, as latent heat of ice formation, is controlled entirely by the thermal properties of the sea ice and the atmospheric conditions. The approach of Stefan (and the empirical equations based on it) assumes that the air temperature is an adequate measure of the atmospheric effects. The relative success of this approach has already been discussed, but it is not very sound theoretically and current investigations are mostly in the direction of measuring the individual energy fluxes between the air and the ice or snow surface to obtain the so-called heat budget of the surface. There are four significant energy fluxes: conductive flux through the ice (Q_K), convective flux in the air (Q_C), radiative flux (Q_R), and heat transfer by mass transport (Q_E) (exaporation or condensation of water substance). The energy balance equation is

$$Q_K = Q_R + Q_C + Q_E \qquad (60)$$

which expresses the fact that the heat reaching the ice surface (during the growth period) must equal the total losses to the atmosphere. A suitable sign convention (such as taking a gain of heat by the ice cover as positive) must be adopted because any of the four Q's may have either sign.

The fluxes Q_K and Q_R can be measured directly with an accuracy of the order of 10% or better, Q_K with a heat flux meter in the ice and Q_R with an all-wave radiometer. At present, the other two fluxes are usually deduced from temperature and wind profiles using the theories of micrometeorology (Sutton, 1953; Priestly, 1959). The validity of some of the equations involved is doubtful and more direct methods would be desirable.

It is well established that in high latitudes the radiative flux Q_R

is the dominant method of heat loss from ice. In a study of the ice on Hudson Bay, Schwerdtfeger and Pounder (1963) showed that although the flux Q_C may be fairly large at any moment, it usually varies cyclically, with energy being lost from the ice during daylight hours and returned to it from the Arctic inversion during the night, so that the 24-hour mean of Q_C is small. They also showed that during the period of ice growth Q_E is negligible at that latitude (60° North) once the ice cover has been established. Evaporation is undoubtedly more significant in warmer climates.

At the present stage of these studies of the heat budget of ice, they do not present a practical method of forecasting ice growth and Stefan's law will continue to be useful. However, the approach is more fundamental and should lead to a better understanding of the processes involved, with ultimate improvement in forecasting techniques.

8.3   The Decay of an Ice Cover

The decay of ice is largely controlled by solar radiation and by the albedo (reflecting power) of the usually snow-covered surface. Growth of the ice stops and decay starts some time before the air temperatures rise to the melting point of the ice. Assur (1956) found that the decrease in thickness Δh (in inches) of Arctic sea ice could be expressed approximately by the equation $\Delta h = E_{10}/30$ where E_{10} is the "warming" exposure in fahrenheit degree-days above 10°F. This equation is obviously not applicable in temperate latitudes where the air temperature falls only rarely below 10°F throughout the winter, but it does emphasize the importance of radiation.

The albedo of snow varies widely, with values of 0·6 to 0·7 being typical of cold snow in settled regions, and values up to 0·9 being applicable in areas such as the Arctic where the fallout of soot and dirt from the atmosphere is negligible. Thus the snow cover reflects a large fraction of the solar radiation incident on it. However, as the intensity of the radiation increases in spring, enough of it is absorbed to start melting of the snow. The albedo of wet

snow is much lower, about 0·45, so that the absorption of radiation is a cumulative and rapid process once it starts. A snow cover
of 20 or 30 cm in the Arctic may melt within two days under the
influence of 24-hour radiation from a sky which is usually cloud-
less at that season. When the snow on an ice cover melts, the wet
ice also has an albedo of 0·5 or so.

In the early stage of ice decay, equation (60) is applicable
usually with positive values for all the fluxes except Q_E. The
equation finds little use, however, because the evaporative term is
important and adequate methods for measuring it have not been
developed. As decay proceeds, the brine cells in sea ice enlarge
and the intercrystalline boundaries in fresh ice melt so that eventually the ice cover contains liquid water throughout and convection of the water becomes possible. There is no adequate theoretical description of the final stages of decay. It is an impressive, even
dramatic, process. A cover of sea ice in the Arctic which is 2 m
thick initially can melt completely within six weeks. A lake may
be covered with 30 cm or more of wet ice one day and completely
free of ice the next. This sudden disappearance of lake ice has
prompted the mistaken idea that ice can somehow become heavier
than water and sink. What usually happens is that a wind storm
breaks up the rotten ice into cakes or floes, overturning some of
them. This mechanical action causes mixing of the water, bringing
some warmer water to the surface, which rapidly melts the remaining ice.

Bibliography

Air Bubbling (1961) Techn. Mem. No. 70 of Associate Committee on Soil and Snow Mechanics, National Research Council, Ottawa.

ANDERSON, D. L. (1960) *Research* (GB) **13**, 310.

ANDERSON, D. L. and WEEKS, W. F. (1958) *Trans. Amer. Geophys. Un.* **39**, 632.

ARMSTRONG, T. and ROBERTS, B. (1956) *Polar Record*, **8**, 4.

ASSUR, A. (1956) *Airfields on floating ice sheets, for routine and emergency operations.* SIPRE (Snow, Ice, and Permafrost Research Establishment) Report 36, U.S. Army Cold Regions Research and Engineering Laboratory, Hanover, N.H. (Further references to reports issued by this organization will simply be listed by SIPRE number.)

ASSUR, A. (1958) In *Arctic Sea Ice*, Pub. No. 598 of the National Academy of Sciences—National Research Council, Washington, p. 106. (Further references to this important report will list it as NAS-NRC Pub. No. 598.)

BACON, G. E. (1955) *Neutron Diffraction*, Oxford, London.

BARNES, H. T. (1928) *Ice Engineering*, Renouf, Montreal.

BARNES, W. H. (1929) *Proc. Roy. Soc.* A **125**, 670.

BERNAL, J. D. (1958) *Proc. Roy. Soc.* A **247**, 536.

BLACKMAN, M. and LISGARTEN, N. D. (1958) *Advances in Physics*, Vol. **7**, No. 26, 189.

BOWDEN, F. P. (1953) *Proc. Roy. Soc.* A **217**, 462.

BOWDEN, F. P. and TABOR, D. (1950) *Friction and Lubrication of Solids*, Oxford, London.

BOYLE, R. W. and SPROULE, D. C. (1931) *Canad. J. Research*, **5**, 601.

BRIDGMAN, P. W. (1914) *J. Franklin Inst.* **177**, 315.

BRIDGMAN, P. W. (1937) *J. Chem. Phys.* **5**, 964.

BROCKHOUSE, B. N. (1958) *Nuovo Cimento Suppl.* **9**, 45.

BROWNE, I. M. and CRARY, A. P. (1958) In *Arctic Sea Ice*, NAS-NRC Pub. No. 598, p. 191.

BUTKOVICH, T. R. (1956) *Strength studies of sea ice.* SIPRE Research Report 20.

BUTKOVICH, T. R. (1957) *Linear thermal expansion of ice.* SIPRE Research Report 40.

CLARK, G. L. (1955) *Applied X-rays*, 4th ed. McGraw-Hill, New York.

COULSON, C. A. (1961) *Valence*, 2nd ed. Oxford, London.

COOK, J. C. (1960) *J. Geophys. Res.* **65**, 1767.

DEBYE, P. (1929) *Polar Molecules*. Reinhold, New York.

145

DITCHEL, W. J. and LUNDQUIST, G. A. (1951) *An investigation of the physical and electrical properties of sea ice*. Bull. Natl. Research Council U.S. No. 122.

DORSEY, N. E. (1940) *Properties of Ordinary Water-Substance*. Reinhold, New York.

FRANK, H. S. (1958) *Proc. Roy. Soc.* A **247**, 481.

FRANKENSTEIN, G. E. (1959) *Strength data on lake ice*. SIPRE Tech. Report 59.

FUKUTOMI, T. (1958) In *Arctic Sea Ice*, NAS-NRC Pub. No. 598, p. 223.

GIGUÈRE, P. A. (1959) *J. Phys. Chem. Solids*, **11**, 249.

GLEN, J. W. (1958) *Advances in Physics*, Vol. **7**, No. 26, 254.

GORDIENKO, P. (1958) In *Arctic Sea Ice*, NAS-NRC Pub. No. 598, p. 210.

GRAYSTONE, P. and LANGLEBEN, M. P. (1963) In *Ice and Snow*, edited by W. D. Kingery, M.I.T. Press, Cambridge, Mass. pp. 114–123.

HERZBERG, G. (1945) *Molecular Spectra and Molecular Structure II. Infrared and Raman Spectra of Polyatomic Molecules*. Van Nostrand, New York.

JACCARD, C. (1959) *Helv. Phys. Acta* **32**, 89.

JELLINEK, H. H. G. (1957) *Tensile strength properties of ice adhering to stainless steel*. SIPRE Research Report 23.

KOLESNIKOV, A. G. (1958). In *Arctic Sea Ice*, NAS-NRC Pub. No. 598, p. 157.

LANGLEBEN, M. P. and POUNDER, E. R. (1963) In *Ice and Snow*, edited by W. D. Kingery, M.I.T. Press, Cambridge, Mass. pp. 69–78.

LANGWAY, C. C. JR. (1958) *Ice fabrics and the universal stage*. SIPRE Tech. Report 62.

LEGGET, R. F. (1958) The Bearing Strength of Ice in *Trans. Engng. Inst. Canada* **2**, 97–142.

LONSDALE, K. (1958) *Proc. Roy. Soc.* A **247**, 424.

MALMGREN, F. (1927) *On the properties of sea ice*. Norwegian North Polar Expedition with the *Maud* 1918–25, Scientific Results, Vol. **1**, No. 5.

MANTIS, H. T. (editor) (1951) *Review of the properties of snow and ice*. SIPRE Report 4.

McCONICA, T. H. (1950) *Sliding on ice and snow*. Report from the American Ski Company to the Research and Development Division, Office of the Quartermaster General, U.S. Army.

MOTT, N. F. and SNEDDON, I. N. (1948) *Wave Mechanics and Its Applications*. Oxford, London.

NAKAYA, U. (1956) *Properties of single crystals of ice, revealed by internal melting*. SIPRE Research Paper 13.

NAKAYA, U. and MATSUMOTO, A. (1954) *J. Colloid Sci.* **9**, 41.

NIVEN, C. D. (1959) *Canad. J. Phys.* **37**, 247.

NORTHWOOD, T. D. (1947) *Canad. J. Research*, A **25**, 88.

OWSTON, P. G. (1958) *Advances in Physics*, Vol. **7**, No. 26, 171.

PAULING, L. (1960) *The Nature of the Chemical Bond*, 3rd ed. Cornell U.P., Ithica.

PEREY, F. G. J. and POUNDER, E. R. (1958) *Canad. J. Phys.* **36**, 494.

PERUTZ, M. F. (1948) *J. Glaciol.* **1**, 95.

PESCHANSKY, I. S. (1957) *Problemy Arktiki*, **2**, 161.

PETERSON, S. W. and LEVY, H. A. (1957) *Acta Cryst.* **10**, 70.

POUNDER, E. R. (1960) *Heat flow in ice sheets and ice cylinders.* International Assoc. Scient. Hydrology Pub. No. 54, 56.

PRIESTLEY, C. H. B. (1959) *Turbulent Transfer in the Lower Atmosphere,* University of Chicago Press, Chicago.

SCHWERDTFEGER, P. (1963) *J. Glaciol.* **4**, 789.

SCHWERDTFEGER, P. (1964) *Gerland's Beitrage zur Geophysik,* **73** 1, 44.

SCHWERDTFEGER, P. and POUNDER, E. R. (1963) *Energy exchange through an annual sea ice cover.* International Assoc. Scient. Hydrology Pub. No. 61, 109.

SHUMSKII, P. A. (1955) *Principles of Structural Glaciology.* Translated by David Kraus, American Meteorological Society. Available from Library of Congress, Washington.

SIMPSON, L. S. (1958) In *Arctic Sea Ice,* NAS-NRC Pub. No. 598, p. 162.

Smithsonian Meteorological Tables (1951). Sixth revised edition. Smithsonian Institution, Washington.

STEPHENS, R. W. B. (1958) *Advances in Physics,* Vol. **7**, No. 26, 266.

SUTTON, O. G. (1953) *Micrometeorology.* McGraw-Hill, New York.

TABATA, T. (1958) In *Arctic Sea Ice,* NAS-NRC Pub. No. 598, p. 139.

VOITKOVSKII, K. F. (1960). *The Mechanical Properties of Ice.* Translation AMS-T-R-391 by American Meteorological Society. Available from U.S. Dept. of Commerce, Washington.

WHITMAN, W. G. (1926) *Am. J. Sci.* **211**, 126.

WYMAN, M. (1950) *Canad. J. Research,* A **28**, 293.

ZUBOV, N. N. (1945) *L'dy Arktiki (Arctic Ice),* Izdatel'stvo Glavsevmorputi, Moscow. (Text in Russian).

Index